Eithne -

Enjoy

The Homekeeper's Diary 2023

FRANCIS BRENNAN

Gill Books

Gill Books
Hume Avenue
Park West
Dublin 12
www.gillbooks.ie

Gill Books is an imprint of
M.H. Gill and Co.

9780717194704

Edited by Alison Walsh
Proofread by Gráinne Treanor
Portrait photography by Barry Murphy
Styling by Ann Marie O'Leary
Designed by iota (www.iota-books.ie)
This book is typeset in Hoefler, DIN
    and Brandon Grotesque
Printed and bound by L.E.G.O. SpA, Italy

For permission to reproduce photographs, the
author and publisher gratefully acknowledge
the following: Stock photography © iStock/Getty
Premium; all other photography © Barry Murphy.

The author and publisher have made every effort
to trace all copyright holders, but if any have
been inadvertently overlooked we would be
pleased to make the necessary arrangement
at the first opportunity.

*The paper used in this book comes from
the wood pulp of managed forests.*

A CIP catalogue record for this book is available
from the British Library.

5 4 3 2 1

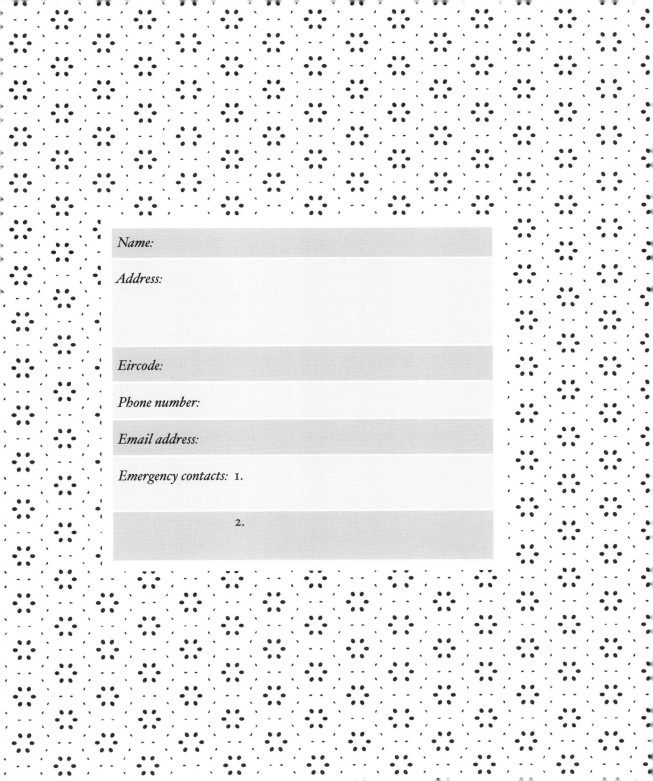

Name:

Address:

Eircode:

Phone number:

Email address:

Emergency contacts: 1.

                         2.

CONTENTS

A NOTE FROM FRANCIS

I'm writing to you from my desk in my new apartment in Kenmare town. It's cosy and compact and I feel as if I'm making a fresh start in life after so many years of living in the countryside. Lots of us have made a fresh start over the past year or two, whether it's moving closer to family or changing job: it seems as if we've all been reassessing what really matters in life. For me, it was about exchanging my lovely garden and house for a lifestyle that is more manageable for me and that has brought me closer to family and friends. I miss my garden, but now I look down on the busy streets of Kenmare and I watch people going about their business and I love it. I feel that I'm connected to life.

Moving was a nightmare, as you can imagine, as I tried to squeeze forty years or so of living into boxes and bags. I had no idea that I'd accumulated so much stuff over the years: suits, ties, shirts, books, ornaments − including my favourite collection of ornamental apples given to me by family over the years. I don't even know how it started, but this collection soon took on a life of its own! I had everything from porcelain to glass to carved wood. Fortunately, I managed to donate the whole lot to Longueville House in Mallow, Co. Cork, which has a cider distillery, but it really did bring home to me that I had too much of everything. So many things came with memories: of holidays I'll never forget, friends I've known for years and the joy of receiving a gift from my nieces and nephews when they were small, but I also knew that even if I didn't have the keyring from Tulum, or the silk tie from Singapore, I'd still have the happy memories.

It was time to clear the clutter and start anew, so in January 2022 I began to sift through my various collections and decide what to keep and what could go. There are only so many sets of napkins that a man can need! But this move represented more than just a clear-out for me; it was about the start of a new phase in life, one in which

I'd do less tidying, cleaning and sorting, and one in which I'd enjoy life's simple pleasures. I was also very conscious of wanting to make my impact on the planet smaller. I grew up in a generation where greaseproof paper was reused, tinfoil was carefully folded and kept in a kitchen drawer, clothes were mended and the house wasn't full of collections of ornamental apples! Then I got used to plastic bags, cling film, convenience food and throwing out my TV if it didn't work. I didn't see anything wrong with it, but now I've come to understand that if I want to see my nieces' and nephews' children grow up healthy and free from worry, I need to do my bit.

After the couple of years we've had, nobody wants a lecture on green living, but to me, it's not about being bullied into recycling, or into travelling everywhere by donkey and cart, it's about making better choices whenever I can, in food, in clothes and in getting around, and finding pleasure in making just a few small changes to my lifestyle for the planet's benefit. I have no idea what 2023 will bring and how many challenges will be in store for us, but I hope it will bring health and happiness to everyone. We all need renewal this year, a sense of hope and a feeling that we are moving forward in our lives again and focusing on the things that really matter. I know that I do!

Wishing you all a healthy, happy 2023.

ESSENTIAL INFORMATION

Health

Doctor	
Dentist	
Health insurance policy number	
PPS number	
Children's PPS numbers	
Name	Number
Name	Number
Name	Number
Name	Number
Local hospital	
Blood group	
Dentist	
Physiotherapist	
EHIC number	expires
Vet	
Pet insurance policy number	

Money

Bank	
Credit union	
Post office	
Credit card helpline	
Overseas credit card helpline	

Around the house

Hairdresser	
Plumber	
Electrician	
Gas company	
Oil supplier	
Nearest Garda station	
Home insurance provider	
Home insurance policy number	

Children

Childminder	
School office	
Children's phone numbers	
Name	Number
Name	Number
Name	Number
Name	Number

Cars

Car registration number		
Breakdown assistance		
Car insurance provider		
Car insurance policy number		
Mechanic		
Nearest NCT testing centre		Test due
Car tax renewal		
Local taxi service		

Work

Office	
Direct line	

Useful websites and numbers

National Car Testing Service	www.ncts.ie	01 413 5994
Department of Foreign Affairs	www.dfa.ie/passportonline/	
Citizens Information	www.citizensinformation.ie	0818 074 000
Irish Rail	www.irishrail.ie	0818 366 222
Bus Éireann	www.buseireann.ie	0818 836 611
Translink NI Railways/Translink Ulsterbus	www.translink.co.uk	028 (048) 9066 6630
Dublin Bus	www.dublinbus.ie	01 873 4222

2023 AT A GLANCE

JANUARY						
M	T	W	T	F	S	S
						1
2	3	4	5	6	7	8
9	10	11	12	13	14	15
16	17	18	19	20	21	22
23	24	25	26	27	28	29
30	31					

FEBRUARY						
M	T	W	T	F	S	S
		1	2	3	4	5
6	7	8	9	10	11	12
13	14	15	16	17	18	19
20	21	22	23	24	25	26
27	28					

MARCH						
M	T	W	T	F	S	S
		1	2	3	4	5
6	7	8	9	10	11	12
13	14	15	16	17	18	19
20	21	22	23	24	25	26
27	28	29	30	31		

APRIL						
M	T	W	T	F	S	S
					1	2
3	4	5	6	7	8	9
10	11	12	13	14	15	16
17	18	19	20	21	22	23
24	25	26	27	28	29	30

MAY						
M	T	W	T	F	S	S
1	2	3	4	5	6	7
8	9	10	11	12	13	14
15	16	17	18	19	20	21
22	23	24	25	26	27	28
29	30	31				

JUNE						
M	T	W	T	F	S	S
			1	2	3	4
5	6	7	8	9	10	11
12	13	14	15	16	17	18
19	20	21	22	23	24	25
26	27	28	29	30		

JULY						
M	T	W	T	F	S	S
					1	2
3	4	5	6	7	8	9
10	11	12	13	14	15	16
17	18	19	20	21	22	23
24	25	26	27	28	29	30
31						

AUGUST						
M	T	W	T	F	S	S
	1	2	3	4	5	6
7	8	9	10	11	12	13
14	15	16	17	18	19	20
21	22	23	24	25	26	27
28	29	30	31			

SEPTEMBER						
M	T	W	T	F	S	S
				1	2	3
4	5	6	7	8	9	10
11	12	13	14	15	16	17
18	19	20	21	22	23	24
25	26	27	28	29	30	

OCTOBER						
M	T	W	T	F	S	S
						1
2	3	4	5	6	7	8
9	10	11	12	13	14	15
16	17	18	19	20	21	22
23	24	25	26	27	28	29
30	31					

NOVEMBER						
M	T	W	T	F	S	S
		1	2	3	4	5
6	7	8	9	10	11	12
13	14	15	16	17	18	19
20	21	22	23	24	25	26
27	28	29	30			

DECEMBER						
M	T	W	T	F	S	S
				1	2	3
4	5	6	7	8	9	10
11	12	13	14	15	16	17
18	19	20	21	22	23	24
25	26	27	28	29	30	31

Bank and Public Holidays in Ireland 2023

Monday 2 January – New Year's Day holiday

Monday 6 February – St Brigid's Day

Friday 17 March – St Patrick's Day

Monday 10 April – Easter Monday

Monday 1 May – May Day bank holiday

Monday 5 June – June bank holiday

Monday 7 August – August bank holiday

Monday 30 October – October bank holiday

Monday 25 December – Christmas Day

Tuesday 26 December – St Stephen's Day

2024

JANUARY
M	T	W	T	F	S	S
1	2	3	4	5	6	7
8	9	10	11	12	13	14
15	16	17	18	19	20	21
22	23	24	25	26	27	28
29	30	31				

FEBRUARY
M	T	W	T	F	S	S
			1	2	3	4
5	6	7	8	9	10	11
12	13	14	15	16	17	18
19	20	21	22	23	24	25
26	27	28	29			

MARCH
M	T	W	T	F	S	S
				1	2	3
4	5	6	7	8	9	10
11	12	13	14	15	16	17
18	19	20	21	22	23	24
25	26	27	28	29	30	31

APRIL
M	T	W	T	F	S	S
1	2	3	4	5	6	7
8	9	10	11	12	13	14
15	16	17	18	19	20	21
22	23	24	25	26	27	28
29	30					

MAY
M	T	W	T	F	S	S
		1	2	3	4	5
6	7	8	9	10	11	12
13	14	15	16	17	18	19
20	21	22	23	24	25	26
27	28	29	30	31		

JUNE
M	T	W	T	F	S	S
					1	2
3	4	5	6	7	8	9
10	11	12	13	14	15	16
17	18	19	20	21	22	23
24	25	26	27	28	29	30

JULY
M	T	W	T	F	S	S
1	2	3	4	5	6	7
8	9	10	11	12	13	14
15	16	17	18	19	20	21
22	23	24	25	26	27	28
29	30	31				

AUGUST
M	T	W	T	F	S	S
			1	2	3	4
5	6	7	8	9	10	11
12	13	14	15	16	17	18
19	20	21	22	23	24	25
26	27	28	29	30	31	

SEPTEMBER
M	T	W	T	F	S	S
						1
2	3	4	5	6	7	8
9	10	11	12	13	14	15
16	17	18	19	20	21	22
23	24	25	26	27	28	29
30						

OCTOBER
M	T	W	T	F	S	S
	1	2	3	4	5	6
7	8	9	10	11	12	13
14	15	16	17	18	19	20
21	22	23	24	25	26	27
28	29	30	31			

NOVEMBER
M	T	W	T	F	S	S
				1	2	3
4	5	6	7	8	9	10
11	12	13	14	15	16	17
18	19	20	21	22	23	24
25	26	27	28	29	30	

DECEMBER
M	T	W	T	F	S	S
						1
2	3	4	5	6	7	8
9	10	11	12	13	14	15
16	17	18	19	20	21	22
23	24	25	26	27	28	29
30	31					

2025

JANUARY
M	T	W	T	F	S	S
		1	2	3	4	5
6	7	8	9	10	11	12
13	14	15	16	17	18	19
20	21	22	23	24	25	26
27	28	29	30	31		

FEBRUARY
M	T	W	T	F	S	S
					1	2
3	4	5	6	7	8	9
10	11	12	13	14	15	16
17	18	19	20	21	22	23
24	25	26	27	28		

MARCH
M	T	W	T	F	S	S
					1	2
3	4	5	6	7	8	9
10	11	12	13	14	15	16
17	18	19	20	21	22	23
24	25	26	27	28	29	30
31						

APRIL
M	T	W	T	F	S	S
	1	2	3	4	5	6
7	8	9	10	11	12	13
14	15	16	17	18	19	20
21	22	23	24	25	26	27
28	29	30				

MAY
M	T	W	T	F	S	S
			1	2	3	4
5	6	7	8	9	10	11
12	13	14	15	16	17	18
19	20	21	22	23	24	25
26	27	28	29	30	31	

JUNE
M	T	W	T	F	S	S
						1
2	3	4	5	6	7	8
9	10	11	12	13	14	15
16	17	18	19	20	21	22
23	24	25	26	27	28	29
30						

JULY
M	T	W	T	F	S	S
	1	2	3	4	5	6
7	8	9	10	11	12	13
14	15	16	17	18	19	20
21	22	23	24	25	26	27
28	29	30	31			

AUGUST
M	T	W	T	F	S	S
				1	2	3
4	5	6	7	8	9	10
11	12	13	14	15	16	17
18	19	20	21	22	23	24
25	26	27	28	29	30	31

SEPTEMBER
M	T	W	T	F	S	S
1	2	3	4	5	6	7
8	9	10	11	12	13	14
15	16	17	18	19	20	21
22	23	24	25	26	27	28
29	30					

OCTOBER
M	T	W	T	F	S	S
		1	2	3	4	5
6	7	8	9	10	11	12
13	14	15	16	17	18	19
20	21	22	23	24	25	26
27	28	29	30	31		

NOVEMBER
M	T	W	T	F	S	S
					1	2
3	4	5	6	7	8	9
10	11	12	13	14	15	16
17	18	19	20	21	22	23
24	25	26	27	28	29	30

DECEMBER
M	T	W	T	F	S	S
1	2	3	4	5	6	7
8	9	10	11	12	13	14
15	16	17	18	19	20	21
22	23	24	25	26	27	28
29	30	31				

Phases of the Moon

New Moon	First Quarter	Full Moon	Third Quarter
		6 January	15 January
21 January	28 January	5 February	13 February
20 February	27 February	7 March	15 March
21 March	29 March	6 April	13 April
20 April	27 April	5 May	12 May
19 May	27 May	4 June	10 June
18 June	26 June	3 July	10 July
17 July	25 July	1 August	8 August
16 August	24 August	31 August	6 September
15 September	22 September	29 September	6 October
14 October	22 October	28 October	5 November
13 November	20 November	27 November	5 December
12 December	19 December	27 December	

Astronomical Events Ireland 2023

Quadrantids meteor shower – 3, 4 January
Hybrid solar eclipse – 20 April
Lyrids meteor shower – 22, 23 April
Perseid meteor shower – 12, 13 August
Partial lunar eclipse – 28/29 October

Names for the Moon throughout the year

January – Wolf Moon
February – Snow Moon
March – Worm Moon
April – Pink Moon
May – Flower Moon
June – Strawberry Moon
July – Buck Moon
August – Sturgeon Moon
September – Harvest Moon
October – Hunter's Moon
November – Beaver Moon
December – Cold Moon

Sunrise and Sunset Times 2023

Dublin	Sunrise	Sunset	Cork	Sunrise	Sunset
1 January 2023	08.37	16.19	1 January 2023	08.39	16.35
1 February 2023	08.07	17.09	1 February 2023	08.11	17.23
1 March 2023	07.11	18.03	1 March 2023	07.17	18.14
1 April 2023	06.56	20.01	1 April 2023	07.07	20.08
1 May 2023	05.48	20.55	1 May 2023	06.02	20.59
1 June 2023	05.01	21.44	1 June 2023	05.18	21.45
1 July 2023	04.59	21.58	1 July 2023	05.16	21.58
1 August 2023	05.39	21.23	1 August 2023	05.54	21.26
1 September 2023	06.32	20.17	1 September 2023	06.43	20.23
1 October 2023	07.24	19.04	1 October 2023	07.32	19.14
1 November 2023	07.24	16.55	1 November 2023	07.26	17.08
1 December 2023	08.14	16.13	1 December 2023	08.16	16.28

Tides 2023

		1 Jan	1 Feb	1 Mar	1 Apr	1 May	1 Jun	1 Jul	1 Aug	1 Sep	1 Oct	1 Nov	1 Dec
Dublin	h/t	07.13 19.29	08.34 21.01	06.41 19.26	09.21 22.08	09.24 22.09	10.11 22.47	10.31 23.00	12.12	01.00 13.32	01.21 13.46	01.16 13.31	01.39 13.48
	l/t	07.13 12.50	01.58 14.29	00.08 12.50	02.57 15.30	02.58 15.29	03.37 16.04	03.51 16.18	05.23 17.40	06.39 18.52	06.56 19.11	06.50 19.15	07.11 19.44
Cork	h/t	00.29 13.04	01.59 14.33	12.36	03.05 15.35	03.15 15.38	03.56 16.18	04.06 16.32	05.38 18.05	06.59 19.23	07.17 19.38	07.10 19.29	07.32 19.50
	l/t	06.55 19.31	08.25 20.57	06.24 19.02	09.31 21.54	09.39 21.58	10.21 22.42	10.32 23.00	12.07	01.11 13.31	01.30 13.49	01.17 13.37	01.34 13.56
Belfast	h/t	06.39 18.49	07.55 20.21	06.00 18.44	08.37 21.28	08.43 21.33	09.33 22.11	09.52 22.22	11.30 23.45	00.16 12.50	00.39 13.07	00.44 13.02	01.10 13.20
	l/t	00.19 12.39	01.37 14.10	12.26	02.28 15.09	02.38 15.15	03.26 15.57	03.42 16.09	05.18 17.34	06.40 18.53	06.59 19.14	06.53 19.18	07.10 19.45
Galway	h/t	00.39 13.01	02.11 14.45	00.06 13.05	03.13 15.54	03.11 15.46	03.46 16.13	04.01 16.25	05.32 17.48	06.41 18.57	06.55 19.13	00.25 12.50	07.07 19.38
	l/t	06.43 19.13	08.26 20.45	06.36 19.14	09.30 21.48	09.22 21.40	09.49 22.11	10.01 22.30	11.26 23.54	00.19 12.36	00.33 12.52	06.46 19.10	00.48 13.17

CONVERSION TABLES

I used to go half mad trying to work out what US cups were in grams and so on, so this handy primer will come in useful for me as well as you! Also, www.onlineconversion.com allows you to convert any measurement.

 HEAT
$°C \times 1.8 + 32 = °F$
$°F - 32 / 1.8 = °C$

 **VOLUME**

Gas	°F	°C	Fan
½	250	120	100
1	275	140	120
2	300	150	130
3	325	160	140
4	350	180	160
5	375	190	170
6	400	200	180
7	425	220	200
8	450	230	210
9	475	240	220

One cup	Imperial	Metric
Caster sugar	8oz	225g
Brown sugar	6oz	170g
Butter	8oz	225g
Flour	5oz	140g
Raisins	7oz	200g
Syrup	12oz	340g

1 TEASPOON = 5ML
1 DESSERTSPOON = 10ML
1 TABLESPOON = 15ML

# WEIGHT
1KG = 35OZ/2.2LB

LIQUIDS

Imperial	Metric
½oz	15g
¾oz	20g
1oz	30g
2oz	60g
3oz	85g
4oz (¼lb)	115g
5oz	140g
6oz	170g
7oz	200g
8oz (½lb)	225g
9oz	255g
10oz	285g
11oz	310g
12oz (¾lb)	340g
13oz	370g
14oz	400g
15oz	425g
16oz (1lb)	450g
24oz	680g
32oz (2lb)	0.9kg
48oz (3lb)	1.4kg
64oz (4lb)	1.8kg

Pint	Metric	Cup	fl. oz
	100ml		3½
	125ml	½	4½
¼	150ml		5
	200ml		7
	250ml	1	9
½	275ml		10
	300ml		11
	400ml		14
	500ml	2	18
1	570ml		20
	750ml	3	26
1¾	1.0l	4	35

WASHING SYMBOLS

Last year, with no launderettes or dry-cleaners open, I became an expert in the art of handwashing and fabric care. Here's a handy primer on the most common symbols.

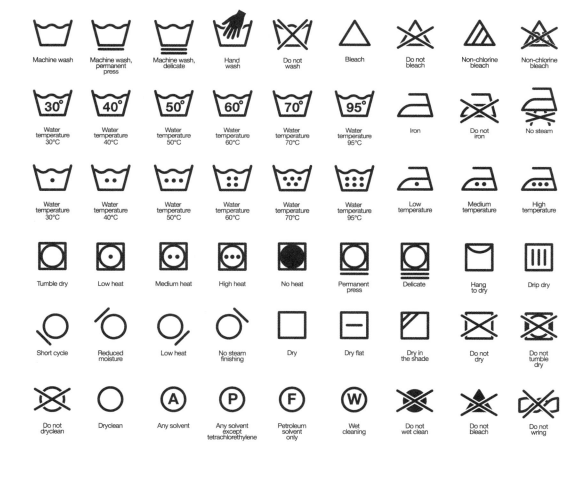

CARING FOR FABRICS

The other thing I learned last year – the hard way – was how to care for delicate fabrics. I had a couple of accidents with shrinking items of clothing, so now I'm careful to (a) check the label and (b) look up a 'how to' so my precious delicates don't end up a shrivelled mess. Here's a handy table of the most common fabrics and how to care for them.

WOOL	SILK	COTTON
Have you ever put a woollen jumper in the wash and taken it out to discover it's like a little ball of felt? I have. Wool should be washed in lukewarm water with a gentle detergent. Don't knead it vigorously or wring it out – a gentle squeeze is best, before shaping your damp woollen item and drying it flat. A friend of mine pops her jumpers in a colander and lets them drip away before doing this, which is very clever.	Again, lukewarm water is best, and a specialist detergent – but before you wash, do a patch test to check that your garment is colour fast. Dampen a little corner of the item and press it into a white towel – if the colour comes off, you'll need to have it dry-cleaned.	I used to wash my cottons in a hot wash, before I discovered that not all cottons are the same. So my nice 100 per cent cotton shirt needs a cold wash, but my cotton bedsheets, underwear and bath towels need a hot one to get rid of any nasties. I also don't tumble dry cotton clothes, because they shrink, and I turn them inside out before washing to preserve them better.

LINEN	ATHLEISURE
I love linen, because it's a gorgeous fabric and it's not that hard to look after. Lukewarm water is your friend, along with a mild detergent. You can wash it in the machine on a delicates setting (although I'd get linen jackets dry-cleaned because of their shape and because the linen might shrink). Dry your linens flat and iron while damp. Don't iron them when fully dry or you'll fix the creases.	Nowadays, so many of us wear this not only to the gym but also in everyday life. However, you don't need to wash it on a hot cycle to get rid of bacteria – if you do, the garments won't last. Cold water is your friend, and provided you wash your garments after exercise and reasonably frequently, germs should not be an issue. A pre-soak with half a cup of white vinegar in cold water will really help with odour. Don't use fabric softener on athleisure, because it damages the fibres, and don't dry-clean it. Instead, roll it in a towel to absorb moisture and then dry it flat.

FRANCIS'S HANDY HOW TO ...

Last week, I noticed that my dishwasher was making a strange gurgling sound. When I opened it, I could see that the drain was blocked with bits of paper from old jam jars that I'd washed for recycling. So I took the paper out and ... it was still gurgling away. Now, once upon a time I'd have been on the blower to my local plumber, or even have decided that the device was past saving, but instead I googled 'my dishwasher won't stop gurgling' and before I knew it, I was down on my hands and knees, a torch in my hand, fixing the problem. And the moral of the story is? Try to fix the problem yourself or get help *before* throwing something out – provided, of course, that it is safe to do so. E-waste is a particular problem – last year, I had to replace my mobile phone in order to use the latest version of an app! I had to throw out a perfectly good device and I found that really galling. But let's focus on what we *can* do!

Fix a smelly dishwasher

1. Unplug it!
2. Lift out the draining basket and give it a good clean – it will often have bits of food and other gunk attached to it. I use hot soapy water and a little bottle brush to really get it clean.
3. Check the spray arms for any blockages and remove them. If you check in your manual, you'll see how to detach and reattach them.
4. Once you've checked for any obvious blockages, you can plug the machine in again. Completely empty the machine of any dishes, cutlery, etc. and place a bowl of vinegar in the top basket. Set the dishwasher to 'hot' and put it through a cycle. Vinegar is great for restoring your machine's shine.
5. Run the cycle again, but this time sprinkle baking soda in the bottom of the machine. It's wonderful at getting rid of pesky smells.

Patch up holes in plasterboard

When I was a youngster, I trained in the Sligo Park Hotel, which came with its own living quarters. Our rooms were ranged either side of a long corridor that led to a door to the main hotel, but some genius had knocked a large hole in one of the walls as a shortcut. To get to the main hotel, all you had to do was to step through it! Needless to say, I went the long way around. This reminded me of the fact that I'm forever getting little dents in the walls at home, from shifting furniture or accidentally knocking into a wall, so I've become a dab hand at fixing them.

1. You will need: a mask and protective plastic goggles in case of flying bits or dust; some fibreglass tape (it looks like a roll of tennis netting); a small bucket; some patching plaster compound, which you'll find in your DIY store; a little palette to smooth the compound over the hole; and some sandpaper or a sanding block.
2. Tidy up the dent or hole and remove any loose plaster – don't make the hole bigger in the process!
3. Place the fibreglass mesh over the hole – this will act as a surface for the plaster compound.
4. Apply your plaster compound or filler, smoothing it over the mesh, and leave to dry. Don't worry if there are rough edges – that's what the sandpaper is for.
5. When the compound is completely dry, gently rub off any sharp bits with your sandpaper.
6. Once the finish is smooth, you are ready to paint over the hole.

Clean a laptop

1. Unplug your device.
2. Give it a very gentle rub with a microfibre cloth.
3. For the screen, your best bet is a specialist screen cleaner. Don't use Windolene or anything like that – it's not suitable for laptop or PC screens.
4. For the keyboard, I use the brush attachment of my vacuum to very gently remove any dirt. If you have a handheld cleaner, that will work too.
5. Get a damp sponge and wring it out so that there is absolutely no excess water. Cool boiled water is ideal. Wipe it gently over the keyboard.
6. A cleansing wipe is also useful, provided it does not contain any harsh cleaning abrasives. Always check your computer manual before you undertake any cleaning.
7. A cotton swab will work wonders at prising loose dirt from around your keys. Be gentle. Don't lift the keys unless you absolutely have to – they can be tricky to put back.
8. Hoover up any loosened dirt with your brush attachment.
9. You can use a dilute solution of rubbing alcohol dabbed onto a cloth to wipe the case. Again, make sure there are no drips from the cloth. Wipe the case with a dry cloth.
10. Compressed air is brilliant for loosening grime in your USB ports.

Keep cut flowers fresh

There's nothing I like better than a vase of fresh flowers on the kitchen table. I try not to buy too many cut flowers, but I'll often make a bouquet with my tulips when they spring up, or with late summer roses. If you are lucky enough to get a present of cut flowers, here's how to make them last a little longer.

1. Snip an inch off the bottom of the stems, so that they will draw up water. Ideally you should cut at a roughly 45-degree angle.
2. Pop them into water as soon as possible.
3. Make sure that any flowers or foliage are above the waterline, or they'll rot.
4. For winter blooms, cool water is best; for summer ones, luke-warm will keep them happy.
5. You can make your own flower food by adding a few drops of apple cider vinegar to the water and a teaspoon of sugar for energy. My mother used to swear by putting a penny at the bottom of the vase, because the copper kept the water clean.
6. Professional florists often keep their bouquets in the fridge overnight, as this makes the flowers last longer. I don't think I could fit a bouquet in my fridge, but I do try to keep it in a cool spot, away from heated radiators, etc.

Use Epsom salts around the house and in the garden

1. Epsom salts are magnesium sulphate by another name. They're not only brilliant for soaking your feet or soothing tired muscles, but a tablespoon mixed with 2 litres of water makes a brilliant plant spray. You can also sprinkle some around your tomato plants to help them grow.
2. The brilliant *Farmer's Almanac* (www.farmersalmanac.com) recommends using a cup of Epsom salts mixed with a cup of lemon juice and about 3 litres of water as a homemade hair rinse. Apparently, it rids the hair of a build-up of products.
3. A mixture of Epsom salts and washing-up liquid is an excellent grout cleaner. Test on a little patch first before you get started.
4. Soaking in a bath of Epsom salts will help soothe sunburn and it also makes for an excellent natural body scrub.

Repair a hole in a sock

I'm forever finding holes at the toes or heels of my socks and, quite honestly, I used to throw them out. However, since I found out how easy it is to mend socks, I've become a dab hand at it, just like my mother used to be.

1. Finding a darning 'egg' changed my life – well, almost! It looks a bit like the handle of a skipping rope, but if you slip it into the sock, it makes the hole stand out and, crucially, means that you are not stitching the hole closed when you repair it. Genius! You can get them from any home store or online.
2. Make sure your sock is inside out.
3. Snip away any loose threads around the area you want to patch.
4. Thread your needle, ideally with thread that doesn't stand out. Don't tie a knot in the end.
5. Starting outside the hole, sew a vertical line of running stitch (pushing your needle in and out of the fibres) upwards, then, without pulling the thread too hard so that it pulls all the way through, go vertically down, then up then down, and so on, until you have a grid pattern that goes right over the hole. Repeat the grid pattern horizontally. What you'll be left with is a mesh that covers the hole, but doesn't leave you with a puckered lump of sock under your foot.
6. Turn your sock the right way around and admire your work!

SHOPPING LISTS

If saving money is essential, or even if you want to simply waste less, consider making a grocery list. Not a scribble on a Post-it note, but something you can update, add to and reshape according to your needs. You can do this by food category (e.g. 'meat', 'pulses', 'dairy', etc.) or by meal planning and buying accordingly.

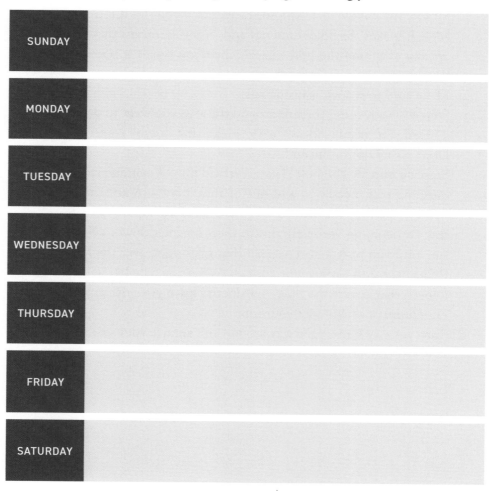

SUNDAY	
MONDAY	
TUESDAY	
WEDNESDAY	
THURSDAY	
FRIDAY	
SATURDAY	

It's a good idea to have a list of things you need (or don't need) on hand. I currently have three jars of coffee and two pats of butter because I didn't take my own advice! A few tips:

- Plan your meals for the week so you know exactly what to buy.
- Decide what your spending priorities are, whether it's organic meat or fresh fish, and buy the best quality that you can afford.
- Keep your larder stocked with basics so there's always something on standby.
- Plan your weekly budget in advance. I'm shopping for one, so it's easy for me. If you have a family, your needs will be greater – but you can still save by buying certain high-cost items, like shampoo and washing detergents, when there's an offer on.
- Familiarise yourself with the aisles of your local supermarket to see what's in stock and how much it costs. Look at the *price per kg* to assess this. For instance, a 2kg bag of apples might cost less than a tray of four, depending on brand.
- If budget is a factor, stock up on tinned pulses and staples like rice and pasta. We all need fresh fruit and veg, but it can be easily wasted. I like to use up all my spare veg on a meat-free Monday.
- I'm a divil for getting distracted in the shop by the lovely things on display, but I have to force myself to stick to the list!
- Look for cheaper or 'own brand' versions of items like tinned tomatoes, where quality isn't such an issue – that leaves you more to spend on other things.
- Nominate one or two days in the month for using up everything in the cupboard before buying more.

Your 'master' meal plan and grocery list might look like this:

PRODUCE	BREAD/BAKERY	DELI	BREAKFAST

BAKING GOODS	CANNED GOODS	CONDIMENTS	SNACKS

REFRIGERATED	MEAT/SEAFOOD	FROZEN	DRINKS

HEALTH/BEAUTY	HOUSEHOLD	MISC.	MISC.

FOOD ON YOUR DOORSTEP

Have you ever tried foraging? You'll probably have done so without even realising. Picking blackberries, field mushrooms, rosehips, even seaweed – all of this is foraging. It simply means picking your own food from the wild. It might surprise you to know that Ireland is rich in plants and berries that are safe to eat and taste delicious. And you'll be all the more satisfied because you picked it yourself! But before you get carried away and run outside, always, *always* check that what you pick is edible. Read up on edible plants before you go, or, better still, go for a ramble with a professional forager so that you can learn about nature's bounty in more detail. A little bit of research will take you to any number of experts who can guide you.

There's a very useful website called www.eattheweeds.com, which explains how to spot and handle many wild edible plants.

So, what can you forage to eat?

In the wild

Dandelion leaves I had a friend who was forever picking up big clumps of dandelion leaves in summer. I thought she must have a great passion for them, until she revealed that they were for her pet rabbits! However, dandelion leaves are edible and easy to spot, with that bright yellow flower. A little nibble will reveal that they taste a bit like rocket. If their flavour is too strong for you, mix them in with milder lettuce varieties. Don't forget to wash them first! Dogs do like 'using' dandelions ...

Curly dock leaves We used to use these as children to relieve nettle stings. A leaf applied to the spot reduced the itching instantly. They are actually very nice in a salad; they have a slight lemony flavour.

They're a bit like kale in that they need to be 'massaged' – with a squeeze of lemon juice – to soften the texture. If you mix them with something like wild mint, they'll be delicious. And speaking of wild mint, you'll know it simply by the taste, which is similar to the domestic variety. And you'll be able to smell it, too! The leaves are narrow and pointed and the flowers are purple.

Nettles I used to meet a man on my walks who would wander along the hedgerows, a plastic bag in hand, snipping the tops off all the nettle plants. When I asked him what he was doing, he replied that he was pinching off the tenderest part of the plant to make nettle soup. Without gloves! He was an expert, but I'd always recommend wearing gloves, because nettles do sting. Once exposed to hot water, their sting is neutralised, so they make a great addition to soup, in place of spinach, for example. Use tongs to pop them into the stock so that you don't get stung.

Wood sorrel I can clearly remember eating this as a child and really enjoying that sharp-sour taste. We'd find it on summer walks in the woods and would nibble away on it. It looks very like clover, but the leaves are a bit looser and more rounded than that plant. You could try using it in a pesto, to make the most of that flavour – just replace some or all of the basil leaves with sorrel, blending it with olive oil, pine nuts and parmesan or pecorino cheese. Wild garlic is another easy-to-find plant that really does smell of garlic.

Bilberries Another great favourite of ours as children were these blueberry-like berries that grow on little, low bushes in the Dublin mountains. Irish people often call them fraughans or fraocháns and they used to grow everywhere, before pine forests took over. I read somewhere that Ireland used to have a very lucrative export business in the fruit, so many did we have. They are harder to find these days, but they are still there in little patches. They look very like blueberries, but they are tarter and more perfumed in flavour. Try using them in place of blueberries, although you might need to add sugar to taste.

Sloes These dark purple berries are the fruit of the blackthorn tree (*Prunus spinosa*), and you'll know them by their appearance – they look like miniature plums – and by the thorns on the tree! Sloes are picked in October and they are very popular in sloe gin, I'm told. It's easy to make at home: you pop your sloe berries into the freezer (this mimics the frost that makes them release their juices), then you get a large bottle, big enough to take 1 litre of gin, 500g of sloes and 250g of sugar. Pop the sloes in first, then the sugar, and finally the gin, and give it a gentle swish. Put away under the stairs and once a week or so give it a little shake. If you make it in October, it should be ready for Christmas, when you open it and strain the sloes off, leaving you with a lovely flavoured gin.

Rosehips When I went to Granny's in Co. Sligo, we would always collect rosehips, the bright red fruit of the wild rose. Rich in vitamin C, the hips would be used for rosehip tea, rosehip oil and rosehip jam, and it was also an ingredient in many natural remedies. In fact, in Britain during World War II, people were encouraged to use them to avoid being deficient in the vitamin due to a lack of other kinds of fruit. They're fiddly enough to pick, as I recall, because you have to pull hard to get the rosehip off the tree. Eaten raw, their seeds give them a nasty bitter taste. But they are transformed in a syrup or tea. If you have the time, try making some rosehip syrup. Pick 1kg of rosehips, wash them and blitz in a food processor. Add them to 3 litres of water, bring to the boil, then strain the pulp through a muslin cloth or fine-mesh sieve, keeping the juice. Return the pulp to the pan and add 1 litre of boiling water, bring to the boil and then leave it for a few minutes, before straining again. You'll now have two bowls of juice, which go back into the pan with 500g of sugar. Reduce this liquid down until you have a fairly thick syrup. When it's cool, pour it into a clean bottle or Mason jar. A spoon of this daily will give you more than enough vitamin C.

By the sea

When I looked into wild foraging in greater detail, I discovered that there are all kinds of things by the seaside that are edible and tasty. I'm a conservative eater – and I haven't forgotten the taste of carrageen! – so I needed a little persuading, but once I'd eaten samphire, which grows wild near the beach, I was converted. The other great thing about seaweed is that it's full of vitamins and minerals, so it's good for you as well as being surprisingly tasty. Make sure that you pick a spot that is pollution-free and not used by dogs. You are safe enough with seaweeds, because they are not generally toxic, but needless to say, *always check that you know exactly what you are eating when it comes to wild food. If in doubt, check with an expert.*

Sea spaghetti Did you know that you can eat spaghetti from the sea? This edible seaweed is easy to spot, because it looks like dark green spaghetti! You see it swishing around in the water near the shoreline. You can cut it – don't uproot it, so that it can keep growing – then simmer or steam it for ten minutes in boiled water, whereupon it will turn a vivid green, and eat it like actual spaghetti. Or you can chop the cooked seaweed and add it to a stir-fry along with your noodles. The thing with seaweed is that a little goes a long way. Try adding it to your normal diet so that you develop a taste for it.

Sea lettuce This is another tasty seaweed. It looks not unlike frisée lettuce, being bright green and with delicate little fronds. Not to be confused with gutweed, which is also bright green, but has more of a stringy appearance. I haven't tasted sea lettuce, but I'm told that the thing to do with it is to dry it, which you can do in the sun, and crumble it over soups and stews, or eat it as 'crisps'!

Dulse or dillisk Dulse is well known for its health-giving properties. It's often used in seaweed baths and is full of iodine. You'll spot it by its reddish-purple hue, and it grows on rocks close to the shore. If you toast it on a dry pan, it tastes like bacon, apparently, and it's not as salty as you might think.

Kelp You'll know this seaweed from its distinctive shape – long, flat ribbons with crinkled edges. You don't need to help yourself to the whole plant; just snip off a section to shred into noodles, or dry it out and blitz it to add flavour to dishes. You can also buy kelp noodles in many supermarkets and speciality shops as a nutritious alternative to wheat-based varieties. The Japanese know it as kombu, and they shred it finely and add it to dashi or broth.

Sea beet You might spot this on the beach itself. It looks a bit like chard or spinach, with quite robust-looking green leaves and reddish stems. You can use it just like spinach, for example wilted and added to omelettes, or you can chop it and add it to a salad or a stir-fry. Its flowers, which are green or reddish-green, are also edible.

Sea purslane Sea purslane has almost cactus-like leaves and long reddish stems. You can boil it until tender, which will make it a bit less salty, or you can eat it raw, if you're adventurous.

Sea radish With its bright yellow flowers and slender stems, sea radish doesn't look much like a radish. But, like radishes, it's a brassica – a member of the cabbage/broccoli family. It has a very distinctive seed pod, a bit like a pointed broad bean pod, and tastes both of radish and cabbage, which sounds interesting!

COOKING AND STORING FOOD

When my mother was cooking for the five of us and Dad, she had a meal for every day of the week. My brother John used to call Monday's dinner – leftovers from the Sunday roast – 'the lonely dinner'; Tuesday was stew; Wednesday was bacon and cabbage; Thursday was lamb's liver; Friday was fish, of course; and Saturday was a stuffed pork loin. On Sunday, we always ate a roast, but rarely chicken, which was a luxury in those days. We did eat well, as you can see, and there was no processed food. Nowadays, we eat less meat, which is a good thing, I think. So, what if you want to cook from scratch? How can you cook and store safely? www.safefood.net is home to advice on food safety. Here are some tips:

Cooking meat

- **Whole cuts** like steak don't have to be cooked all the way through, because the bacteria sit on the outside. However, minced meat needs to be cooked all the way through, as does chicken and pork.
- **Cook your steak** on a very high heat to 'sear' it (and kill bacteria) on the outside, so the inside is nice and pink.
- **Cook chicken thoroughly**. Mum's mantra was always 20 minutes per pound weight plus 20 minutes – i.e. 20 minutes per 450g plus 20 minutes. Check that the chicken's cooked by piercing it with a skewer at the thickest point, like the thigh, and check that the juices run clear. If in doubt, slice into it and check that there are no traces of pink.
- **Defrosting chicken** should take 24 hours for a 2.5kg bird – in the fridge. Put any defrosting meat on a large plate to catch any drips that could get onto food below.

- **Hens' eggs** can be eaten raw (if you really must!), say in mayonnaise, or lightly cooked, if you are a healthy adult. Older people, babies and the immunocompromised should not eat raw eggs. Duck eggs have a higher risk of salmonella, so cook these thoroughly – in 'raw-egg' recipes, like mayonnaise or tiramisu, use hens' eggs.
- **Use separate chopping boards for meat and vegetables**.
- **Wash your hands** thoroughly before and after handling food.

Foods where extra care is needed

Homemade stock Chill quickly and then put it in the fridge. Make sure it's piping hot if reheating.

Shellfish Only buy shellfish from a trusted source; cook it as fresh as you can; discard any with *open shells* before you cook them. When they are cooked, discard any with *unopened* shells. Oysters should be plump and shiny and retreat from your finger when you poke them.

Raw milk and cheese Don't serve to elderly people or youngsters. Pregnant women should avoid them because of the risk of listeria bacteria.

Rice Cook it properly, serve it quickly. If you are reheating it, cool it down quickly, because bacteria can grow at room temperature – I spread it out on a tea tray to cool it, then refrigerate it immediately. When reheating it, make sure it's piping hot. Only reheat rice once.

Chilled foods These need to be handled with more care than frozen foods, because they go off more quickly. Pay attention to the 'use by' dates on these products. Pack/bag them separately from the rest of your shop, so they don't get warm. Store in the fridge – away from fresh foods – and make sure you use them by the 'use by' date. Cook chilled foods until they are piping hot.

Fish Buy fish that is as fresh as can be – nice bright eyes and a shiny skin are good signs of freshness. You don't have to cook it all the way through. According to www.safefood.net, the bacteria is on the outside of the fish, so the inside can be 'pink' if the outside is well cooked.

RECYCLING – THINGS YOU MIGHT NOT KNOW

- The good news is that soft plastics can now be recycled. According to www.mywaste.ie, the following can now go into your green bin: Bread wrappers, fruit/veg and salad wraps and bags, kitchen/ toilet roll outer wrap, breakfast cereal bags, plastic shopping/carrier bags, dried fruit/seed and nut bags, frozen food bags, pasta/rice/noodle bags, cheese packs (outer wrap), baked goods/confectionery outer wrappers, crisp/cracker wrappers, bubble wrap, electrical item/white goods/appliances bags/ wrap, mattress/pillow wraps, wet wipes (outer wrap), detergent/ dishwasher bags, garden compost/chipped bark bags.
- You can recycle tins, paper, cardboard and rigid plastics.
- Rigid plastics like bottles and yoghurt cartons, as well as tins, need to be cleaned first, as contamination is a big problem in recycling. If you have one dirty container in a batch, it can contaminate the whole lot.
- Make sure that you don't squish everything tightly into the bin: www.mywaste.ie suggests that your recycling should be 'clean, dry and loose'.
- For electronic devices, consult www.mywaste.ie or WEEE Ireland at www.weeeireland.ie/household. They have a handy map of centres and retailers where your waste electrical devices can be returned.
- You can donate matching pairs of old shoes (I tie mine together at the laces), clothes and certain soft furnishings (not old sheets or pillowcases) to charity shops and clothing bins. Clothes banks will take more damaged items, which will be shredded and recycled.
- Many councils now offer furniture removal services that will collect certain large items from you. There is a fee, but it beats a fine for littering!

- There used to be a 'little man' in every street in Ireland who repaired hoovers, washing machines, cookers, even televisions. Those days are gone, but thankfully, the idea of repairing rather than replacing is taking off again. Repair My Stuff (www.repairmystuff.ie) has a list of places that will repair your devices – everything from lawnmowers to tablets.
- The freecycle movement – www.freecycle.org – has lots of local groups devoted to recycling unwanted items, such as baby equipment, garden furniture, etc. Many communities have set up freecycle groups on WhatsApp.
- Food waste is a big issue in the Western world, where approximately one-third of our food is thrown out. Imagine! According to My Waste, 25 per cent of our water is used to produce food that will never be eaten. The food-sharing app Olio has been introduced to Ireland recently, and you can use it to offer unwanted food, such as pasta or teabags, and find items that you want for free. What a brilliant idea!
- According to My Waste, Ireland is Europe's top producer of plastic. Oh dear. Let's all try to improve on that. During the pandemic, single-use cups and bottles were necessary, but recently, I have dug out my 'keep cup' for coffee and a reusable bottle for water. I keep a little tote bag in the car for when I visit local shops, and I also bought a very handy couple of net bags for fruit. Now I buy loose fruit in the shops and put it in my bags, thus avoiding plastic.
- Your local health food store will often have 'refill stations' where you can fill up on household products. There are also some refill stores where you can buy food in bulk. Online stores are great for bulk-buying, say, shampoo, but make sure that the formula works for you before you buy 5 litres of it.
- I didn't realise how fast 'fast fashion' really is. Some of the larger retailers get daily shipments of new clothes and you can get a

catwalk look within a matter of weeks. And most of what we buy is dumped. So what can we do about it? The Rediscovery Centre in Dublin – the National Centre for the Circular Economy – gives classes in sewing, repairs and even knitting. See www.rediscoverycentre.ie. Sustainable fashion brands help us to shop without a guilty conscience, but much of what they offer is more expensive. Look for pre-loved clothing: it's not just for the charity shops any more, and there are some very good online sources of pre-loved wedding dresses, bags, shoes and even designer handbags. Some department stores have introduced clothing-rental schemes, so that you can rent a *gúna* for a wedding without stressing over the cost and the fact that you'll never wear it again!

My best recycled and eco-friendly products

DAYS OUT AROUND IRELAND

Over the last couple of years, we've all become much more outdoorsy than we used to be, and it would be nice to think that we'd keep it up, even now that indoor attractions open once more. So I decided to include some open-air trips and spots for you to visit, to keep up the good work! *It's wise to call ahead or double-check to ensure that the attraction is open.*

Dublin and Leinster

- *St Anne's City Farm and Ecology Centre*, Raheny – a real glimpse of farm life for city kids. They can admire hens, goats, chickens and pigs as well as learn about growing produce. And it's free! www.st-annes-city-farm-and-ecology-centre.business.site
- *Newbridge House and Farm*, Donabate, is another working farm and you can visit the grounds as well as the house. There's also an adventure playground. www.newbridgehouseandfarm.com
- If you like grand homes, *Castletown House* in Celbridge, Co. Kildare looks very imposing, but it's the grounds, which slope down to the River Liffey, that are the real draw here. It has tons of space for the little ones to run around, as well as a pleasant courtyard area for tea and coffee.
- *Powerscourt Estate*, Co. Wicklow – lots to do here (activities are separately ticketed), with the waterfall, the gardens, the distillery and the Cool Planet Experience, a climate-action exhibition. www.powerscourt.com
- In Bray, *Mount Usher Gardens* are well worth a visit, as they have some gorgeous plants and trees, pleasant tearooms and a garden centre. www.mountushergardens.ie

- *Newgrange*, Co. Meath. I can still remember visiting Newgrange years ago and being able to walk straight across the fields to the site. Nowadays, it's a lot more organised, but a day trip is well worth the effort. There's a shuttle bus to ferry you between the sites, a guided tour and exhibits. Amazing to think that it was built in 3200 BC – before the Pyramids and Stonehenge! www.worldheritageireland.ie. Don't forget to visit the *Hill of Tara* on your way home. It's so atmospheric.
- *Lough Boora* is a lovely discovery park in Tullamore, Co. Offaly. It's full of ponds and wildlife as well as the remains of the former Bord na Móna peatworks. You can walk the many trails and hire bikes, and there's a café and visitor centre. www.loughboora.com
- *Athlone Castle*, Co. Westmeath – this impressive castle, smack bang on the River Shannon, was defended by Colonel Richard Grace from the Williamite forces after the Battle of the Boyne. www.athlonecastle.ie
- *Heart-Shaped Lake*, Co. Wicklow – one for the instagrammers! It's a corrie lake – a glacial lake to you and me – and it's off the Old Military Road. It is indeed shaped like a heart and it looks spectacular. However, it does involve a stiff hike up Tonelagee Mountain, and it can be mucky, so not for the faint-hearted or for young children.
- Not as well known as its neighbour, the Wicklow Way, *St Kevin's Way* is a 30km route following the path of the saint himself from Hollywood, Co. Wicklow, to Glendalough. As you pass through the Wicklow Gap, the scenery is spectacular, and when I visited, it was still much quieter than the more popular routes. There's a lovely little story about St Kevin's Bed, which is on the route, but which is inaccessible. Apparently, the saint was fast asleep when a maiden came to visit, and he threw her into the lake nearby to

show her that he was indeed a saintly man! www.pilgrimpath.ie; www.wicklowmountainsnationalpark.ie/st-kevins-way/

- *Old Rail Trail* – this lovely trail stretches from Mullingar to Athlone, a distance of about 40km, following the old railway beside the canal. This trail is ideal for families, because there are lots of entry and exit points, so you can do smaller sections, say Athlone to Moate, which is just 8km. Dún na Sí Heritage Park, near Moate, has lots of natural attractions, from the site of an old hedge school to a wetland park. www.athlone.ie /visit/dun-na-si-amenity-and-heritage-park/

- *Cú Chulainn's Castle*, Co. Louth – sadly, this isn't his actual castle, but the ruins of a house near Dundalk which was apparently built by a pirate! It's known as Castletown or Dún Dealgan Motte. Rumour has it that the house is built on the remains of the birthplace of Cú Chulainn, hence the name. www.visitlouth.ie /explore-and-do

- *South Leinster Way* – A good long route for more enthusiastic walkers, this will take you from Kildavin, Co. Carlow to Carrick-on-Suir, Co. Tipperary, a distance of 102km. The countryside is very pretty here, and you'll skirt Mount Leinster on your way. Some of the Way is on the River Barrow, which is lovely, and there are also some really attractive villages to visit, such as Inistioge and Graiguenamanagh, with its open-air pool in the river. www.discoverireland.ie/carlow/the-south-leinster-way

- I love the gardens and arboretum at *Woodstock*, Co. Kilkenny. They are just outside the arty village of Inistioge. They have everything, from summerhouses to yew walks to rose gardens, and are a must for anyone who loves gardens and nature. www.woodstock.ie

Munster

I'm beginning here with Kerry – and why wouldn't I? I love my adopted home and think it has so much to offer, but then I'm biased!

- I love visiting the house and gardens in *Kells Bay*. Their micro-climate means that they have all kinds of plants that grow nowhere else, and you'll see spectacular examples here of tree ferns and other exotics. It's also home to Ireland's longest rope bridge and it has a nursery and rooms. www.kellsbay.ie
- *Crag Cave* is one that the children will love. Thought to be a million years old, this limestone cave was only discovered in 1983. It has wonderful rock formations and is huge, so you can spend the day exploring. There is also a café, playground and bird of prey display. www.cragcave.com
- *Ballaghbeama Gap* – this isn't as crowded as the Ring of Kerry, being more 'off the beaten track', but it is just as attractive, with gorgeous mountain scenery, lakes and bogland. Beware, it is a very winding road, and single-lane, so allow plenty of time for manoeuvres and drive with caution. You will be rewarded by some spectacular views.
- *Skellig Michael* has become such a draw over the last few years that you could be waiting an age to visit, but if you want to see beehive huts without the sheer drop, take a detour to *Fahan*, on the Dingle peninsula, where you can see other examples of these amazing little houses. You can visit *Derrynane House*, home of Daniel O'Connell, and there's a lovely beach nearby. www.derrynanehouse.ie
- If you don't fancy the Cliffs of Moher, I like the cliffs in *Portmagee*, which are spectacular and from which you can see the Skelligs. You can also walk a pilgrim trail, *Cosán na Naomh*, which is 18km from Ventry beach to Brandon Mountain, west of Dingle. It's quite a rugged walk, so make sure you are well prepared.

- In West Cork, the *Beara-Breifne Way* marks the long march of O'Sullivan Beara and his troops after the Battle of Kinsale, where he lost to Queen Elizabeth I – and it is *long*, 500km in all, stretching from the Beara peninsula all the way to Blacklion, Co. Cavan. Apparently, of O'Sullivan's 1,000 troops, only 35 finished the march, so you have been warned! You can do little sections of the way, but you'll need to do your research to find out which sections are the most developed and open as 'waymarked trails'. You can find a county-by-county guide to all walking trails, complete with information on grades and general advice, at www.sportireland.ie/outdoors/walking/trails; and www.toughsoles.ie has a blog devoted to the walk.
- At the very tip of the Beara Peninsula lies *Dursey Island*, which you can visit by cable car. It's tiny – just a few kilometres in length and about 1.5km wide – but it's a great place for bird-watching. You can see guillemots, razorbills, even puffins, which is a real thrill, and it's a great spot to see whales. Even better is *Bull Rock*, off Dursey Island, which is home to a large colony of gannets. It's well known in the area for the lighthouse, built in the nineteenth century, and for the extraordinary archway cut into the rock face. A boat tour will take you out. As I write, the famous Dursey Island cable car is being repaired, but did you know it's the only cable car in Europe that crosses open sea? www.durseyisland.ie
- *Sherkin Island* is another lovely place, very popular with summer visitors. A highlight is the regatta, usually held at the end of July. Unlike Dursey, Sherkin has a couple of pubs, a church and a primary school for its year-round population of 100. Right in the middle of Roaringwater Bay, the island is a ten-minute ferry ride from Baltimore Harbour, so easily accessible. It's known for the arts, as well as its rich marine life. If you keep your

eyes peeled, you might see our native lizard there, but the sea is teeming with life: dolphins, basking sharks and even minke whales are often spotted. And if you're really lucky, you might spot the elusive fin whale, which is second only to the giant blue whale in size. www.sherkinisland.ie; www.sherkinisland.eu

- *The Ewe Experience* is described as 'Ireland's only interactive and interpretative sculpture garden'. Near Glengarriff, Co. Cork, it's a quirky, lively combination of art and nature. www.theewe.com

- Moving on to Waterford, the *Greenway* will take you on your bicycle from Waterford City to Dungarvan along the old railway route. I tackled it last year and it was relaxing and full of families enjoying themselves. The countryside is lovely, and you'll come across Mount Congreve Gardens, a full 70 acres of gardens near Waterford City; you'll pass the Comeragh Mountains; and you'll also see Dungarvan Bay and its lovely beach, Clonea Strand, as well as the Durrow Tunnel, which is 382 metres in length – it's no longer in use, by the way, so you can walk down its quiet, echoey length quite safely. www.greenwaysireland.org/waterford-greenway

- You can't visit Waterford without learning about its Viking heritage. King of the Vikings is a virtual reality experience, and there's also Waterford Treasures, an impressive museum of all things medieval. There's great food to be found in this part of the world, and Waterford City was voted Ireland's food destination 2019, with its own tapas trail, Waterford Harvest Festival and Dungarvan's food festival in spring. www.kingofthevikings.com; www.waterfordtreasures.com

- *Ardmore Cliff Walk* is a lovely, easy cliff loop walk, just 4.5km in length. It's part of St Declan's Way, and you'll pass a holy well dedicated to him, after the famous Cliff House Hotel. Keep an eye out for the shipwreck! It's not very old, in case you're thinking of pirates – it ran aground in 1988 and has been there ever since. You'll also see the remains of old watchtowers, one from World War II and one that dates from the Napoleonic Wars, according to local website www.ardmorewaterford.com. Just a little way off the loop lies St Declan's Monastery, well worth a visit.

- *St Declan's Way* is the full 96km route. It brings together several old pilgrimage paths and will take you from Ardmore to Cashel in Co. Tipperary. It takes in an ancient route called the Rian Bó Phádraig, or the path of St Patrick's Cow, which she apparently dug out with her horns! It's said that St Declan walked the route to meet St Patrick in the fifth century. Waterford is such a pretty county and the rugged Knockmealdown Mountains are very picturesque. Arriving in Cashel, you feel very like the old pilgrims who used to walk this route and many others. www.stdeclansway.ie; www.pilgrimpath.ie

- *Tountinna*, Co. Tipperary is a relatively easy mountain climb in Portroe. Known as the Graves of the Leinstermen Loop, the name is exciting enough! It refers to the King of Leinster and his men, who met a sticky end at the hands of Brian Boru's wife Gormlaith in the year 1000. She ambushed them as they climbed over Tountinna and the king himself is buried there. You'll see Lough Derg in all its glory from the top of this little mountain, as well as the counties of Galway, Tipperary, Clare and Limerick. Worth the climb!

Connacht

- I was very proud to read that Mum's native Co. Sligo had bid for UNESCO World Heritage Status. This is because there are no fewer than 85 Neolithic sites in the county, including the passage tombs at Carrowmore, Knocknashee and Carrowkeel.

The Glen, Culleenamore, Co. Sligo is a little valley stuffed full of flora and fauna on the side of Knocknarea mountain. You can also climb the mountain easily and visit Queen Maeve's Grave, which was a great favourite of ours as children.

- The *'Lake isle of Innisfree'* can be viewed from a boat trip on Lough Gill, near where my mother lived for many years. When I'm in Co. Sligo I also love to visit *Drumcliff*, where Yeats is buried. The churchyard is idyllic, with a view of Ben Bulben. My brother Damien has transformed my mother's family farm into a homestead and does a tour called the Yeats Experience – www.yeatssligoireland.com

- I remember visiting *Mullaghmore*, Co. Sligo, on *At Your Service* with John a few years ago, and it was lovely. It has great water sports facilities and Bundoran and Strandhill are close by. Mullaghmore has huge waves, so it's also something of a surfing hotspot.

- *Downpatrick Head* in north Co. Mayo is a revelation. The cliffs are terrifying, but the sea stack that stands just offshore is a wonder. It's called Dún Briste and legend has it that St Patrick hit the cliff with his staff, causing the sea stack to break away. That fellow got everywhere! Mass is celebrated here in his honour on the last Sunday of July. You'll also see the Stags of Broadhaven, a range of huge, pointed rocks that stick out of the bay. Beyond the pretty village of Ballycastle, you'll come to *Céide Fields*, the world's oldest field system at more than 6,000 years old. It's incredible to think that our ancestors were farming in this organised way so many years ago. www.heritageireland.ie/ceide-fields

- The *Erris peninsula* has a lovely looped walk and is a haven for water sports; and UISCE, near Belmullet, provides tuition as Gaeilge for teens in kayaking, windsurfing and so on.

- The *Great Western Greenway* (often referred to as the Mayo Greenway), a track between Westport and Achill Island, is spectacular and winds along for 42km of lovely safe cycling. (www.greenwaysireland.org/great-western-greenway) You can also walk from Newport to Bangor Erris on a walking trail.

- Moving on to Co. Galway, the food scene in *Galway City* is something else, with restaurants like Aniar, Loam, Ard Bia and so on, but Galway is also a great city to wander around, with its little laneways and coffee shops and the nearby strand at Salthill. The International Arts Festival in July is a huge event.

- If you like island-hopping, *Inis Meáin* is the quietest of the Aran islands, an alternative to *Inis Mór* and *Dún Aonghasa*, which can be busy in summer. *Inis Meáin* is home to Teach Synge, the restored cottage of playwright John Millington Synge. *Inis Oírr* is tiny, just two square miles, but has lovely beaches, and you can hire a bike to see it all.

- *Inishbofin* is also a lovely day trip from Cleggan pier in Connemara. Ferries sail regularly from the pier to the island, which is tiny, but packed with history and activities, including a regatta and an arts festival.

- Also in Connemara is the wonderful *Derrigimlagh Bog*, on which Marconi built his first wireless station and which has been transformed into a lovely outdoor museum and looped walk. Alcock and Brown crashed into this bog in 1919 on the first non-stop transatlantic flight – they survived, and there's a monument on top of Errislannan Head close by, with views of the Twelve Bens mountain range. And if you feel like climbing a mountain, *Diamond Hill* in the Connemara National Park is very popular. It has a very well-maintained path, but it's steep near the top! Worth it for the views of Kylemore Abbey below. The Abbey itself is a nice day trip, with a well-tended walled garden, a restored Gothic church and many cafés. There's also a little bus if the children get tired of walking.

- Everyone knows that Donegal has some of the best beaches in the country, like *Portsalon* beach, but it also has some wonderful ruggedness. *Slieve League* has some of the highest cliffs in Europe – three times the size of the Cliffs of Moher! *Fanad Head* lighthouse looks across to the Inishowen Peninsula, home to Malin Head, Ireland's most northerly point, and very wind-swept and spectacular. The beach near Fanad, *Ballymastocker Bay*, has been voted the world's 'second most beautiful beach' according to Discover Ireland. *Glenveagh National Park* is huge and full of lovely walking trails. You can also climb *Errigal*, in Gweedore, a mere 750 metres high! It will take you about four hours, but there is some scrambling involved, so come prepared – and watch out for the weather.

- I love the sound of *Turas Cholmcille*, an ancient pilgrim pathway that takes visitors around 14 standing stones in the valley of St Colmcille, just like the stations of the cross. St Colmcille's Day is 9 June, when local people gather to pay homage to the saint. According to www.pilgrimpath.ie, it's called 'an Turas' and 'is performed barefoot around 15 standing stones and cairns including the saint's own church and bed .... It takes around three hours to complete, and the first Turas is usually performed at midnight of "Lá an Turais" (Day of the Journey).' Some of this pathway is on private land, however, so it's best to check what sections are open and can be visited.

- *Doon Fort* sits right in the middle of Loughadoon, near Ardara, a very impressive drystone fort that once housed the O'Boyle Clan. A local heritage group has been working to remove ivy from the fort to preserve it, and a boat trip around it will show you how impressive it is.

- *Derry* is a lovely town, steeped in history, and a walk around the old walls of the town will give you a real sense of the place. There's a craft village in the city and the Museum of Free Derry tells the story of the city during the Troubles – www.museumoffreederry.org. Not too far away is Mussenden Temple, on a spectacular cliff overlooking the sea – it was built as a library and is based on a temple in Rome.
- Further east, *Belfast* is a compact and interesting city, full of things to see, from the well-known *Titanic Experience* and W5 science experience (www.w5online.co.uk) to the Victorian *Linen Hall Library*, which has a range of tours and events and is a lovely building. If you want to get out and about in the city, *The Troubles Tour* is a guided walking tour of the city, led by both Republican and Loyalist former political prisoners, and the famous *Black Taxi* tours will take you to all of the significant places.
- *Rathlin Island*, 10km off the coast of Co. Antrim, has a mysterious history. Robert the Bruce is meant to have hidden here after being exiled from Scotland in 1306. About 160 people live on the island all year round, but the numbers swell in summer. The *Boathouse Visitor Centre* will tell you all about the history of the island and it's also a paradise for birdwatchers. Look out for puffins between April and July. www.rathlincommunity.org is a fount of information on the island.
- Apparently, David Cameron went for a swim in *Lough Erne*, Co. Fermanagh, when the Lough Erne resort hosted the G8 summit in 2013. If that isn't temptation enough, there are many islands to explore in this watery area, including *Devenish Island*, with its sixth-century monastery and round tower. There's a road bridge to *Boa Island* – it's named not after the snake, but after Badhbh, goddess of war. You can also get to *White Island* via ferry to admire the carvings on the ruined church.

Also in Fermanagh is the *Stairway to Heaven*, or the *Cuilcagh-Legnabrocky Trail* to give it it's proper name. You can take a refreshing hike on the Cuilcagh boardwalk after visiting the Marble Arch caves, a spectacular maze of limestone caves. www.marblearchcaves.co.uk

- If you have the stomach for it, the *Gobbins Cliff Path* in Islandmagee is spectacular, taking you through a series of caves and walkways high above the churning water. www.thegobbinscliffpath.com
- In Co. Down, you can visit the lovely *Mourne Mountains* and scale the Hen, Cock and Pigeon Rock (it's not a rock, it's a mountain!) for the views, or take a guided tour of Slieve Gullion. www.walkni.com/mourne-mountains

MY TRAVEL NOTES

2023

Fresh Starts

In the hotel business, you have to constantly update and renew in order to offer people the very best in comfort and service. Last year, we were lucky enough to be able to use the long periods of hotel closure to our advantage and to refurbish the Park Hotel Kenmare. Now it looks brighter and fresher than ever. We were lucky, I know, because so many people have suffered over the past couple of years: losing jobs, loved ones ... it's been a very tough period for so many people. My own health challenges have prompted me to think about my priorities in life and I always come back to friends and family. Without them, where would I be?

So how can we make 2023 better for us and those we love? My New Year's resolution for 2023 is to focus on spending time with friends and family and on getting a little bit of joy back in life. I realise now, more than ever, that every moment counts and that nothing matters more than those we love.

2 Monday BANK HOLIDAY

'You're allowed to be both a masterpiece and a work in progress.' *Sophia Bush*

3 Tuesday

4 Wednesday

5 Thursday

6 Friday NOLLAIG NA mBAN

7 Saturday

After the indulgence of Christmas, I don't want to eat anything heavy. Simple, nourishing food will do nicely – not forgetting a nice treat, which can be healthy too! I love to make chewy cereal bars, using puffed rice (Rice Krispies), dried apricots, dark chocolate drops, oats and a nut butter, like peanut or almond butter.

8 Sunday

Spellbound

I love this poem, because it reminds me of sitting by the fire in my old home near Sneem, trying to muster the courage to go out in the cold to get a few more logs to keep it going on those long winter evenings.

> The night is darkening round me,
> The wild winds coldly blow;
> But a tyrant spell has bound me
> And I cannot, cannot go.
>
> The giant trees are bending
> Their bare boughs weighed with snow.
> And the storm is fast descending,
> And yet I cannot go.
>
> Clouds beyond clouds above me,
> Wastes beyond wastes below;
> But nothing drear can move me;
> I will not, cannot go.

Emily Brontë

9 Monday

'Home is where you are loved the most and act the worst.'
Marjorie Pay Hinckley

10 Tuesday

11 Wednesday

12 Thursday

13 Friday

Unlucky for some! While no one is entirely sure where
this superstition came from, it was known in Norse
mythology, when a gathering of 12 gods was interrupted
by a gatecrasher – Loki, the bad sibling of Thor. That
made unlucky 13.

14 Saturday

15 Sunday

There's nothing I like better at this time of year than a warming stew.
I find that spices like ras-el-hanout really liven things up without
burning the mouth off me. You can buy it from most supermarkets
nowadays and, if you can't find it, you can make your own, using a
teaspoon each of cumin, coriander, turmeric, a few cloves, a half
dozen cardamom pods (ground) and a little pinch of ginger.

16 Monday

17 Tuesday

18 Wednesday

I try to get out for a brisk winter walk at this time of year. After Christmas and in the dark days of the New Year, it really helps to lift the gloom. Even if it's raining, I just wrap up well, put on my boots and off I go. I spend the first ten minutes moaning, but I always feel better afterwards.

19 Thursday

20 Friday

21 Saturday

22 Sunday

Fun Green Things to Try in 2023

Make bread instead of buying it. We don't have to get ourselves in a tizzy about lamination or yeast! A simple brown wholemeal bread will do nicely, such as this lovely recipe from Safefood (www.safefood.net).

Ingredients

425g wholemeal flour
1 dessertspoon wheatgerm
1 dessertspoon bran
275ml buttermilk
1 tsp bread soda
1 tsp brown sugar
2 tsp polyunsaturated oil, such as sunflower oil
1 medium egg

Method

1. Preheat the oven to 180°C/160°C fan/gas mark 4.
2. Thoroughly mix all the ingredients together.
3. Pour the lot into a lightly oiled 2lb loaf tin.
4. Bake for 15 minutes, then reduce the heat to 150°C/130°C fan/gas mark 2 and bake for a further 40 minutes.

23 Monday

'January ... the Monday of months.' *F. Scott Fitzgerald*

24 Tuesday

25 Wednesday

26 Thursday

'Sometimes a year has been so disastrous and so terrible that entering a new year will automatically mean entering a wonderful year!' *Mehmet Murat ildan*

27 Friday

28 Saturday

29 Sunday

'All sorrows are less with bread.'
Miguel de Cervantes Saavedra

Lá Fhéile Bríde

According to the National Museum of Ireland – Country Life in Castlebar, the traditional food on this day was a meal of potatoes and fresh homemade butter, with perhaps some cabbage to make colcannon. Making St Brigid's crosses was of huge importance. If you had a cross in your home, the saint would bless it for the coming year. Apparently, you could tell how old a house was by the number of St Brigid's crosses attached to the roof beams. Householders would sometimes get a visit from the Biddy Boys, dressed in straw, who would carry a St Brigid's doll made of the same material. They would recite a rhyme:

> Here is Brigid dressed in white.
> Give her a penny for this dark night.
> She is deaf, she is dumb.
> For God's sake, give her some.

If you'd like to find out more, and make your own cross, try the museum's website: www.museum.ie/ga-IE/News /St-Brigids-Day

30 Monday

31 Tuesday

February

1 Wednesday LÁ FHÉILE BRÍDE

2 Thursday

'When you come to the end of your rope, tie a knot and hang on.'
Franklin D. Roosevelt

3 Friday

4 Saturday

In the USA, February is 'Adopt a Rabbit' month, as well as National Embroidery and Chocolate Lovers' month, for obvious reasons.

5 Sunday

How many times did I hear my mother tell me to switch off the lights when leaving a room? I've lost count. But did you know that, according to greennews.ie, 20 per cent of energy is used in lighting? Think of what we could save if we simply switched off when we didn't need it. Mothers are always right!

Fun Green Things to Do in the Garden

Make your own Wormery

I have a friend who loves fishing, so he has a nice big wormery, into which he throws his food waste, which also gives him an endless supply of worms. And there's no smell. It's a win–win! If you're keen to get rid of food scraps and you'd like to give a wormery a go, you don't have to spend money on one of the kits in the garden centre. You can quite easily make your own. The Irish Peatland Conservation Council has a very handy page on making one: www.ipcc.ie/advice/composting-diy/composting-using-a-wormery. If you have children, making a wormery in a – recycled! – bottle or glass jar is a great little project.

If you are handy at DIY, you can make one out of an old plastic box or bin. You drill a few holes in the bottom to drain off the watery waste (you can use it in your garden). Spread a layer of gravel on the bottom, followed by some cosy bedding for your worms – torn-up newspaper or egg boxes and some lovely mouldy leaves. You can get a supply of worms online or from a fishing-tackle shop and you're good to go.

6 Monday BANK HOLIDAY

'Ar scáth a chéile a mhaireann na daoine.' / 'People live in each other's shadows.' (*Irish proverb*) This means that people are better together. How true.

---

7 Tuesday

---

8 Wednesday

---

9 Thursday

After my initial burst of enthusiasm, I tend to flag at this time of the year, when it seems as if winter will never end. Last year, I decided to plant flowers and shrubs that would come up in February, like crocuses, snowdrops and Daphne, to add cheer. At least the new owners of my former home will love them!

10 Friday

---

11 Saturday

---

12 Sunday

The birthday of Abraham Lincoln, Charles Darwin and President Cearbhail Ó Dálaigh.

'February is the border
between winter and spring.'
Terri Guillemets

St Valentine:
The Irish Connection

I always knew that we could lay claim to this romantic saint, but I hadn't realised that our connection to him is so close. The third-century martyr, who was executed by the Romans, was buried in Rome on 14 February, hence the date of his feast day. However, his relics lie in Whitefriar Street Church in Dublin. According to the church itself, a Carmelite by the name of John Spratt went to Rome to preach in the early nineteenth century. So impressed were the locals by his sermons that great crowds gathered to see him. He was given the relics of the great saint by none other than Pope Gregory XVI to take home to Ireland. This he did with great ceremony, but when Fr Spratt died, the relics were packed away until the 1960s, when a proper shrine was built to St Valentine. To this day, couples come to the shrine to pray for happiness in their lives together. You can find all you need to know about visiting this place at www.whitefriarstreetchurch.com. You might also like to know that St Valentine is the patron saint of beekeepers!

13 Monday

14 Tuesday ST VALENTINE'S DAY

15 Wednesday

16 Thursday

17 Friday

18 Saturday

At this time of year, I can catch up on my reading, selecting a historical novel or thriller from the pile of books beside the bed. I also love to read *National Geographic* magazine, to which I've subscribed since 1980. When I moved house, I donated my collection to the National School in Tahilla. They told me that the children would get great use out of it.

19 Sunday

The Fairies (extract)

One of my favourite poems, *The Fairies*, always reminds
me of primary school in Milltown, where I'd sit at my
desk and recite the verse with the rest of the class.

> Up the airy mountain,
> Down the rushy glen,
> We daren't go a-hunting
> For fear of little men;
> Wee folk, good folk,
> Trooping all together;
> Green jacket, red cap,
> And white owl's feather!
>
> Down along the rocky shore
> Some make their home,
> They live on crispy pancakes
> Of yellow tide-foam;
> Some in the reeds
> Of the black mountain-lake,
> With frogs for their watchdogs,
> All night awake.

William Allingham

20 Monday

'Without Valentine's Day, February would be ... well, January.'
Jim Gaffigan

21 Tuesday SHROVE TUESDAY

Time for pancakes! I know this is heresy, but I prefer the thick, fluffy American-style ones to the thin crêpes. Whisk 2 eggs with 50g sugar, add 50g melted and cooled butter and 250ml milk. Mix together 200g plain flour with 3 tsp baking powder and ½ tsp salt and gently add to the wet ingredients. Dollop large spoonfuls onto a hot pan and enjoy with your favourite toppings!

22 Wednesday

23 Thursday

24 Friday

25 Saturday

26 Sunday

27 Monday

'In February, there is everything to hope for and nothing to regret.' *Patience Strong*

28 Tuesday

March

1 Wednesday

'March comes in like a lion and goes out like a lamb.' *Proverb*

2 Thursday

3 Friday

I love the forced pink rhubarb that you can find in the shops now. I'll eat it in a crumble, roasted in the oven with a spritz of orange juice, then served on soft slices of toasted brioche; and I'll even make curd out of it, using rhubarb instead of lemon or orange – the rhubarb cuts through the sweetness.

4 Saturday

5 Sunday

Fun Green Things to Do with Winter Vegetables

I find it hard to shop seasonally because there is such a variety of veg in the shops. Why wait until summer for tomatoes, when I can eat them right now? However, since the pandemic, I've come to understand that shopping locally means that I can support local businesses and farms and reduce those pesky food miles – and the food will be tastier. Think about how delicious strawberries are in June, or asparagus is in May. If you are keen to shop seasonally, Bord Bia has a very good calendar to help you: www.bordbia.ie/whats-in-season.

Winter veg might not seem all that exciting, but purple-sprouting broccoli is delicious steamed and dressed with a knob of butter and a squeeze of lemon. Chard is even more so – and it's as hardy as anything, so easy to grow. My 'hero' veg at the moment is cauliflower: I love to cut it vertically into thick 'steaks', which I marinate in a mild spice mix (1 tsp each of cumin, coriander, turmeric; 2 tbsp olive oil and the juice of a lemon) and roast in a hot oven until it's nice and charred. Delicious!

6 Monday

'As you slide down the banisters of life, may the splinters never point in the wrong direction.' Described by many Irish-American sources as an Irish blessing!

7 Tuesday

8 Wednesday

As I'm away from home a lot, I've decided to create a little garden full of all-green plants on my patio. They will thrive on just a little watering and are suited to the climate here; things like yucca, ivy, New Zealand tree ferns. I'm guaranteed greenery all year round!

9 Thursday

10 Friday

11 Saturday

12 Sunday

When You Are Old

Being a Sligo woman, my mother loved Yeats, and this was one of her favourites.

> When you are old and grey and full of sleep,
> And nodding by the fire, take down this book,
> And slowly read, and dream of the soft look
> Your eyes had once, and of their shadows deep;
>
> How many loved your moments of glad grace,
> And loved your beauty with love false or true,
> But one man loved the pilgrim soul in you,
> And loved the sorrows of your changing face;
>
> And bending down beside the glowing bars,
> Murmur, a little sadly, how Love fled
> And paced upon the mountains overhead
> And hid his face amid a crowd of stars.

William Butler Yeats (1865–1939)

13 Monday

'It is spring again. The earth is like a child that knows poems by heart.' *Rainer Maria Rilke*

14 Tuesday

On this day in 1964, Jack Ruby was found guilty of the murder of Lee Harvey Oswald, the man who shot JFK. In 1883, 14 March marked the death of Karl Marx and, in 1879, the birth of Einstein.

15 Wednesday

16 Thursday

17 Friday ST PATRICK'S DAY

18 Saturday

19 Sunday MOTHER'S DAY

20 Monday

'always it's Spring and everyone's in love and flowers pick themselves'
e.e. cummings

21 Tuesday

22 Wednesday

23 Thursday

24 Friday

25 Saturday

26 Sunday

The clocks go forward by an hour, marking the start of British Summer Time. A British builder by the name of William Willett is thought to have come up with the idea, suggesting that the clocks move forward by 20 minutes every Sunday in April. A British MP even introduced a bill in parliament to this effect, but the farmers opposed it.

Suits Me

When I moved house, I had to downsize my suit collection, which I found hard. I'm a great man for a good, well-fitting suit and I'd had some of mine for years. A classic suit never looks out of date and can be livened up with a smart tie or pocket square. You don't need to be 'bet' into the thing for it to look nice! Here are my top tips for keeping your suits fresh:

- Only wear a suit one day a week and rotate it with your other suits. Suits need to rest if they are not to get baggy and shapeless. If money is an issue, buy one jacket and two pairs of pants, so that you can alternate them.
- Hang your suit on the back of the bathroom door when you are showering to freshen it and keep it from creasing.
- A trouser press will save you a fortune in dry cleaning – and it'll help your trousers last longer.
- If you drive a lot, buy a suit without a vent at the back, so that you don't get that creased flap when you get out of the car.

27 Monday

'I can't believe it's already time to put off my spring cleaning until next year.'
Anonymous

28 Tuesday

29 Wednesday

I always dread the spring clean but feel much better after I've done it and the house is fresh, well aired and sparkling. I concentrate on doing a few big jobs and leave the small ones for my weekly clean. I clean the oven and fridge and turn the mattresses on the beds, and I wash the windows because they are thick with grime after the long winter. I also give the walls a wipe, because you'd be amazed at what can gather on the surface: dog hair, dust, etc.

30 Thursday

31 Friday

1 Saturday

April

2 Sunday

*A classic suit never
looks out of date.*

April Fools

I really enjoy looking out for April Fool's stories in the paper and on the radio and TV. They always give me a laugh. When I looked into this tradition, I found several brilliant examples, such as the 1957 *Panorama* programme, narrated very seriously by Richard Dimbleby, on the Swiss spaghetti harvest. It included pictures of families picking spaghetti off trees – it fooled a surprising number of people, who rang in enquiring about where they could get a spaghetti tree.

I also loved the story about a bogus app, SeeMyGull, which allowed people to track seagulls and report them to their friends before they stole their lunch! This was the brainchild of *The Journal* and, joking apart, city dwellers will confirm that it's a good idea! (I noticed recently that an Australian pub was using a sheepdog to run up and down outside, chasing the seagulls away.) Meanwhile, Supermac's announced the arrival of the bacon and cabbage pizza and Cork IT's website turned black and white, with an announcement that students would need a licence to view it in colour!

3 Monday

'Have nothing in your house that you do not know to be useful, or believe to be beautiful.' *William Morris*

4 Tuesday

5 Wednesday

Passover begins at sundown this evening.
Today is also the 15th day of Ramadan.

6 Thursday HOLY THURSDAY

7 Friday GOOD FRIDAY

A friend of mine who comes from the Basque country cooks up a big vat of tomato-based fish stew on Good Friday. You can make this budget friendly by using whatever white fish is cheapest at the shops (cod, hake, haddock) and a few mussels (discard any open ones). Make a tomato sauce using a couple of tins of tomatoes, a chopped onion, some garlic and a good glug of white wine. Add a pinch of paprika and a teaspoon of fennel seeds, bubble away for 20 minutes and add the fish for the last few minutes. Add a few boiled potatoes to make it stretch.

8 Saturday HOLY SATURDAY

9 Sunday EASTER SUNDAY

Easter Delights

I love Easter more than Christmas, because spring is my favourite season. It's so bright and fresh and so enjoyable to be outside. And I love chocolate! I'm a Christian, so I also love the ceremony that surrounds this special week. Interestingly, countries all over the world have some form of Easter celebration, whether it's religious, such as the spectacular processions of southern Spain, or tied to the seasons, such as in Papua New Guinea, where Easter Sunday cigars are handed out after church.

In Australia, instead of chocolate bunnies they have started to make chocolate bilbies. They do this to draw attention to the fact that this very cute rabbit-like creature (also known as a bandicoot) is almost extinct in that country. In Finland, children dress up as witches on Easter Sunday and go around with broomsticks chasing Satan away. In Greece, all Easter eggs are red to symbolise the blood of Christ, and in Romania they make a beautiful baked cheesecake called pască, which is filled with a rich mix of ricotta cheese, dried fruit and liqueur. In Guatemala, giant carpets are made out of flowers or fruit and laid out on the streets. However, my favourite Easter tradition happens in Norway, where people rush to bookshops to buy the latest crime novels!

10 Monday EASTER MONDAY

'You know you're getting old when you stoop to tie your shoelaces and wonder what else you could do while you're down there.' *George Burns*

11 Tuesday

12 Wednesday

13 Thursday

The birthday of Nobel Laureate Samuel Beckett. Along with his literary achievements, Beckett was also a hero of the French Resistance during World War II and was awarded the Croix de Guerre by the French government.

14 Friday

15 Saturday

16 Sunday

The Compact Vegetable Garden

At this time of year, I miss my garden, but I know that for every loss there is a gain. That's life. This year, I'm determined to concentrate on what I can do, not on what I can't. I have a sunny balcony in my apartment and it's big enough for me to try a few new things. All I need is the following:

- *Decent soil.* If you don't have good soil, try growing veg in containers, so you can fill them with good-quality soil and compost. My wormery provides me with lots of that!
- *Regular water.* Last year, I grew tomatoes, and they were doing very well thanks to daily watering. But then I went away for a week ... When I came back and started watering again, I noticed that the skin on my little tomatoes had burst open. This is what happens if you take a break from watering. They tasted fine, but lesson learned. This year I've made my own watering system.
- *Sunshine.* You need it to grow things like tomatoes and peppers, but if you don't get a lot of sun you can still grow lovely salad leaves, herbs or dark leafy greens like the delicious cavolo nero.

17 Monday

'Kind words can be short and easy to speak, but their echoes are truly endless.' *Mother Teresa*

18 Tuesday

19 Wednesday

Time to handwash my sweaters. I always handwash them in warm water with a gentle detergent. I roll them in a towel to get the water out, then I dry them flat. I love their fresh smell when they are dry.

20 Thursday

21 Friday

22 Saturday

23 Sunday

For every loss
there is a gain.

Sheep and Lambs

This poem by Irish poet Katharine Tynan (1861–1931) sees a spiritual aspect in the arrival in spring of the new lambs, something I look forward to seeing every year.

All in the April evening,
April airs were abroad;
The sheep with their little lambs
Passed me by on the road.

The sheep with their little lambs
Passed me by on the road;
All in the April evening
I thought on the Lamb of God.

The lambs were weary and crying
With a weak, human cry.
I thought on the Lamb of God
Going meekly to die.

Up in the blue, blue mountains
Dewy pastures are sweet;
Rest for the little bodies,
Rest for the little feet.

But for the Lamb of God,
Up on the hill-top green,
Only a Cross of shame
Two stark crosses between.

All in the April evening,
April airs were abroad;
I saw the sheep with their lambs,
And thought on the Lamb of God.

Katharine Tynan (1861–1931)

24 Monday

'Hide not your talents. They for use were made.
What's a sundial in the shade?' *Benjamin Franklin*

25 Tuesday

26 Wednesday

I've recently made the switch from using shampoo,
and the plastic bottles it comes in, to washing my
hair with a solid shampoo bar. It looks like soap,
smells delicious, lasts ages – and there's no plastic
involved. What's not to like?

27 Thursday

28 Friday

29 Saturday

30 Sunday

Easily Foxed

A lovely fox was a regular visitor to my garden in Sneem and I used to leave water out for him, along with bits of fruit. However, I know that feeding foxes and other wild animals is often a subject of some contention, particularly in built-up areas. The Irish Wildlife Trust (www.iwt.ie/foxes) has some pointers for living with *Vulpes vulpes*, to give them their proper name. They suggest that if you do like to feed them, don't do so too close to the house, or they'll begin to associate your house with delicious food! They also advise on no account to hand feed foxes, because becoming overfamiliar with humans can be dangerous to them and a nuisance to us.

They thrive on protein-rich food, including raw meat and even dog food. If this is off-putting, try nuts or even little pieces of cheese. One excellent suggestion is to feed them at the same time every day so they'll appear at that time for a takeaway and the food won't be left out for other nuisance visitors.

1 Monday MAY DAY

The Irish have a long history with this day. Apparently, we used to collect yellow flowers, such as buttercups, primroses and cowslips to decorate the house and keep the *cailleach* (or witch) away.

2 Tuesday

'Is treise an dúchas ná an oillúint.' / 'Nature is stronger than nurture.'
Irish proverb

3 Wednesday

4 Thursday

5 Friday

6 Saturday

7 Sunday

Spring Greens

I'm trying to reduce my meat consumption, and finding nice things to do with veg becomes much easier at this time of year. Asparagus, broad beans, peas, lamb's lettuce ... the choice is endless and very welcome after a winter of root veg!

I love a salad made with simple roasted asparagus and parmesan shavings to make the very most of this gorgeous vegetable's short season. I also stir steamed, chopped asparagus spears into pasta along with a squeeze of lemon juice, some crème fraîche and a glug of the pasta cooking water.

Broad beans are so delicious, as well as being healthy. I like to add them to a quinoa salad or even make a broad-bean hummus. Falafel made with broad beans or fava beans is also delicious; mash broad beans with cooked onion and garlic, cumin and coriander, roll the mixture into little patties and bake them in the oven. You can also make a pesto out of just about any vegetable. My favourite is rocket and walnut pesto, because of its rich greenness.

8 Monday

'A day without laughter is a day wasted.' *Charlie Chaplin* Chaplin used to be a regular visitor to Kerry and holidayed in Waterville for many years. He would stay at Huggard's, which is now known as the Butler Arms, and was regularly seen fly-fishing in the area.

9 Tuesday

10 Wednesday

11 Thursday

There's something about the long, bright evenings in May that makes me want to eat lighter dishes. I'm partial to some cold cooked salmon, dressed with a ginger and chilli mix, served with avocado and ribbons of cucumber with a sprinkling of sesame seeds.

12 Friday

13 Saturday

14 Sunday

15 Monday

'Folks, I don't trust children. They're here to replace us.'
Stephen Colbert

16 Tuesday

17 Wednesday

My father's birthday. I remember clearly one year when the snow on the ground was a foot thick on Dad's special day. As a result, I never put down any summer plants until Dad's birthday has passed!

18 Thursday

19 Friday

May is a great month to wash and air heavy things, like duvets and pillows, which would otherwise take an age to dry. I normally entrust my winter duvet to the cleaners now and pop my summer one on the bed. I reverse the process in October, leaving plenty of time for the duvet to air after washing.

20 Saturday

21 Sunday

Companion Planting

This is a wonderful new idea that isn't really new at all. For years, keen gardeners will have known that certain plants work very well when planted close together, and others don't. However, the practice of companion planting takes this idea up a level by working out which plants can actively help others to thrive. Fernhill Garden Centre in Athlone has some excellent tips for this practice (www.fernhill.ie/garden-tips/12/companion-planting):

- Insects rely on their sense of smell to tell them which plants will be delicious, so if you distract them with another smelly plant, you'll put them off. Fernhill mentions that planting marigolds around your tomato plants might keep whiteflies away. And garlic planted under your roses will put off the aphids – it seems drastic, but effective!

- On the other hand, plants that attract pollinating insects can really help their neighbours: lavender planted at the base of fruit trees, for example, or sweet peas behind courgette plants. What's more, these combinations will look lovely. My mother used to plant nasturtiums around her broad bean canes to deter her enemy, the blackfly, and their bright colours were a tonic.

22 Monday

'The days are long, but the years are short.'
Gretchen Rubin

23 Tuesday

24 Wednesday

The birthday of Queen Victoria, footballer
Eric Cantona and Bob Dylan.

25 Thursday

26 Friday

27 Saturday

28 Sunday

29 Monday

'Never lose sight of the fact that the most important yardstick to your success will be how you treat other people.' *Barbara Bush*

30 Tuesday

31 Wednesday

Teriyaki trout has become my go-to in my efforts to buy fish sustainably. I love teriyaki sauce, which you can buy at the supermarket, or make your own by mixing a teaspoon each of sweet chilli sauce, honey, sesame oil, soy sauce, and a good drop of sherry. A grating of ginger root completes the marinade. You can bake your trout in this light sauce and the results will be deliciously sticky!

June

1 Thursday

2 Friday

3 Saturday

How I love June! The brighter evenings, lighter foods and the warmth of the sun really cheer me up. I make a vow to myself to be outside as much as possible at this time of year.

4 Sunday

Lots of Lovely Strawberries

My cousin Johnny Brennan, of the famous Milltown Christmas trees, used to be a strawberry broker, the middleman between farm and shop, and we all used to work for him during the strawberry harvest. For many of my nieces and nephews, it was their first summer job. Johnny was a fair employer, but one day my niece Fiona tested his HR skills to the limit.

A punnet of strawberries weighed about a pound (or half a kilo) at the time, and a tray of strawberries was made up of ten punnets. However, a tray cost two euro less than ten separate punnets. Fiona thought that this didn't make sense and pointed it out to Johnny.

'Why does a tray cost ten euro and ten punnets cost twelve euro?' she asked.

Johnny looked as if he was giving this some thought. 'What age are you, Fiona?' he asked eventually.

'Oh, I'm fifteen,' Fiona said brightly.

'And what age are you supposed to be to work?' (legally, this is!)

'Sixteen,' she muttered.

'Pick strawberries,' Johnny said. Fiona was silent for the rest of the day!

5 Monday JUNE BANK HOLIDAY

'You know you're getting old when you get that one candle on the cake. It's like, "See if you can blow this out."'
Jerry Seinfeld

---

6 Tuesday

---

7 Wednesday

---

8 Thursday

---

9 Friday

I love macerated strawberries. This simply means stirring a spoonful of sugar into quartered and hulled berries and leaving them to sit for a while, so that you get lovely pink juices. Eat with Greek yoghurt or even ricotta cheese with a sprinkling of flaked almonds for a light summer dessert.

---

10 Saturday

---

11 Sunday

The Green Summer Garden

When pesticides and weedkillers first arrived, they seemed like a godsend. I thought that the only way to get rid of pesky weeds and pests was to nuke them with a handy spray. Now, you'll be glad to know, I am a lot better informed about the dangers, both to myself and to the planet, of using them. To find solutions, I've returned to nature:

- I set beer traps for my slugs. Not very nice, but it works – and they die happy!
- I get rid of weeds on the patio by using a weed burner. You have to be a bit careful when you're lighting it, but I must admit to a certain amount of satisfaction seeing the weeds wither! Alternatively, applying boiling water to them works, and for my flower beds, good old-fashioned hoeing is just the ticket.
- When I was reading the paper one day, I noticed that Diarmuid Gavin advises gardeners to turn a blind eye to things like nettles, thistles and docks, because they attract butterflies and other endangered insects. I'm going to give it a try this year.

12 Monday

'To reconnect with nature is key if we want to save the planet.'
Jane Goodall

13 Tuesday

14 Wednesday

15 Thursday

16 Friday

Today, Bloomsday, is the day in which James Joyce's hero Leopold Bloom began his walk around Dublin in 1904, in *Ulysses*. Joyce's masterpiece was published in 1922 by Sylvia Beach, but was ignored for many years, so much so that in 1924, in hospital after an eye operation, he wrote: 'Today, 16 June 1924 twenty years after. Will anybody remember this date' (https://jamesjoyce.ie/bloomsday). If only he knew.

17 Saturday

18 Sunday FATHER'S DAY

Heating Heaven

We all fell in love with patio heaters during the pandemic, but they can be environmentally unfriendly and they're expensive. I read an article in the *Guardian*, which scared the life out of me; apparently, my patio heater was emitting as much pollution as a speeding truck! It was time to get my house – or patio – in order!

You can always put on an extra layer or use a blanket, but are there any eco-friendly heaters out there? Infrared would seem to be the best choice, as it's cheaper and an electric heater is better for the environment than gas. However, an environmental study of heating devices in Vancouver restaurants and bars revealed that cushions that could be heated in the microwave are more sustainable, as are heated jackets/blankets that simply require a charger to keep them going. I can only imagine what the chef in the Park Hotel Kenmare would think if we used his microwave to heat cushions! Not to mention the fact that they all have to be regularly sanitised to keep germs at bay.

19 Monday

'All truly great thoughts are conceived by walking.'
Friedrich Nietzsche

20 Tuesday

21 Wednesday

Midsummer's Day – the longest day of the year. There are many traditions associated with this day, particularly the lighting of bonfires. In Sweden, people eat pickled herring and salmon and wear crowns of flowers while they dance around a maypole; in Latvia, they leap over a bonfire; and in Spain and Austria they also light fires. In Russia, swimming is popular, as is throwing flower garlands onto water. In Ireland, this special day is a full nine-and-a-half hours longer than midwinter!

22 Thursday

23 Friday

24 Saturday

25 Sunday

26 Monday

'You know you've reached middle age when you're cautioned to slow down by your doctor instead of by the police.' *Joan Rivers*

27 Tuesday

28 Wednesday

29 Thursday

30 Friday

July

1 Saturday

2 Sunday

Adlestrop

Even though Edward Thomas was a Welsh poet, this could just as easily be a poem about the Irish country-side in summer. Sadly, Thomas was killed in World War I.

Yes. I remember Adlestrop—
The name, because one afternoon
Of heat the express-train drew up there
Unwontedly. It was late June.

The steam hissed. Someone cleared his throat.
No one left and no one came
On the bare platform. What I saw
Was Adlestrop—only the name

And willows, willow-herb, and grass,
And meadowsweet, and haycocks dry,
No whit less still and lonely fair
Than the high cloudlets in the sky.

And for that minute a blackbird sang
Close by, and round him, mistier,
Farther and farther, all the birds
Of Oxfordshire and Gloucestershire.

Edward Thomas (1878–1917)

3 Monday

4 Tuesday

On 4 July 1776, the United States became independent from Great Britain. Until this date, the King's birthday had been celebrated every year, but in 1776 many people held symbolic funerals for the monarch, to celebrate his departure!

5 Wednesday

6 Thursday

7 Friday

8 Saturday

9 Sunday

Magical Mackerel

A friend of mine went out fishing in Connemara with a neighbour one evening and caught two hundred of them! Before you panic, he only kept a handful for dinner. The rest were returned safely to the sea.

Citrus works really well with mackerel, as it cuts through the oiliness. One of my favourite ways to cook it is to clean it, then to fill it to bursting with lemon and lime slices. A little salt and pepper and a quick wrap in tinfoil – or newspaper if you prefer – then into the oven it goes for 20 minutes or so (200°C/180°C fan/gas mark 6 should do it).

If you want to try something new, saba shioyaki, or salt-grilled mackerel, is very popular in Japan. All you need to do is salt a mackerel fillet generously on both sides, then place on a frying pan (medium heat) for four minutes or so on each side. The Japanese eat this with daikon radish, but grated fresh turnip or parsnip is a good substitute.

10 Monday

11 Tuesday

12 Wednesday

The last thing I want to do in summertime is to clean. Thankfully, I'm fairly low main-tenance in my new apartment. A friend of mine with a large family divides up the domestic chores when her children are off school and college and can do their bit. She also swears by line-drying to save on electricity – when it's not raining! – and she keeps a weather eye on fruit flies, placing a net cloche over her fruit bowl to keep them away. She also fills her larder with bay leaves to deter pesky pests, because they dislike the smell.

13 Thursday

14 Friday

15 Saturday

16 Sunday

17 Monday

'Live in the sunshine, swim the sea, / Drink the wild air's salubrity'
Ralph Waldo Emerson

18 Tuesday

I try to get out as much as possible these days to make the most of the last days of summer. I'll head off to Kells Bay or one of our county's many other gardens, taking a picnic with me. I keep things simple: cheese, bread, fruit and something nice to have with my flask of hot tea. A friend of mine makes the most delicious Oxford Lunch fruitcake, the recipe for which is a secret, she tells me. I managed to persuade her to share it with all of you! Take a look at November and see if you'd prefer it to a heavy Christmas cake.

19 Wednesday

20 Thursday

21 Friday

22 Saturday

23 Sunday

Summer Mocktails

I have never been a drinker, but I've noticed recently that more and more of my friends are cutting back on their consumption, usually for health reasons. The great thing is that there are so many alternatives for those of us who don't like a tipple – and summer is a great time for refreshing 'mocktails' – with all of the flavour and none of the booze!

- I love iced tea, and prefer to make my own. I like to use half a dozen lemon and ginger teabags, 2 tablespoons of sugar (or alternative sweetener) and 1.5 litres of hot water for the base. I steep the teabags for ten minutes or so, then whip them out and leave the tea to cool. I add lots of citrus slices, a couple of ginger slices, a couple of sprigs of mint and lots and lots of ice.

- A nohito is a mojito without the rum, but with the same delicious flavour. I mix a little sugar with crushed mint leaves in my pestle and mortar and add these to broken-up ice. I divide the juice of four limes between two glasses, then top up with soda water.

- The espresso martini is the drink of the hour at the moment, so if you'd like to make an alcohol-free version, just brew a small pot of your favourite coffee (ideally 50ml real espresso) and add vanilla syrup. (You can make this by reducing 200ml water, 200g sugar and a tablespoon of vanilla extract to a syrup, then leaving it to cool.) Fill your shaker with ice, add two parts espresso, one part vanilla syrup and an equal amount of water and shake. Decorate with coffee beans and enjoy!

24 Monday

'Bend with the tree that will bend with you.'
Irish proverb

25 Tuesday

26 Wednesday

27 Thursday

28 Friday

My mother had a thing about horseflies, and I used to think she was overreacting, until I got a nasty bite from one of them. They are to be avoided, as are midges, my personal bugbear. Midges don't like light-coloured clothing, and you can spray your clothes with repellent as well as yourself. If you hate Deet, try citronella, which has a pleasant smell. Ticks are also a nuisance during the summer and have been known to carry Lyme disease. Don't panic, however: simply check yourself, children and dogs for them after a walk and pinch them out. They'll be visible!

29 Saturday

30 Sunday

Lúnasa

In Celtic times, the beginning of August was considered to be the start of autumn and of the harvest season. The Order of Bards, Ovates and Druids (www.druidry.org) tells us that the festival celebrates the God Lugh, who became synonymous with the harvest because his foster mother, Tailtiu, brought agriculture to Ireland. She was buried in Tailteann, Co. Meath. Dr Karen Ward of Dublin City University tells us that this is the origin of the Tailteann Games, which started around 1600 BC and ended with the coming of the Normans in the twelfth century

Nowadays, the athletic feats which would have been part of the original games, along with trading and match-making, have made a comeback, with festivals around the country holding swimming races and walks. In my own county, Kerry, there's a pilgrimage to the foot of Mount Brandon and, of course, Puck Fair in Killorglin. I watched a lovely archive piece on the RTÉ website on the origins of the fair, including the catching of the famous fair billy goat, which apparently took months in 1976! There's an alarming picture of the goat being hoisted on a special crane high above the crowds, but we were assured that as soon as the fair was over, he would be returned to his mountain home.

31 Monday

'Too much of a good thing can be wonderful.'
Mae West

August

1 Tuesday

2 Wednesday

3 Thursday

4 Friday

5 Saturday

The birthday of Neil Armstrong, the first man
to set foot on the moon.

6 Sunday

The Last of the Courgettes

I had a friend whose mother used to grow courgettes in her vegetable patch way back in the 1970s. Her neighbours thought this was terribly exotic! Courgettes are one of the easiest vegetables to grow, even if you don't have a large garden, because they also come in smaller varieties suitable for pots.

Courgette fritters are a firm favourite, because they make the most of their flavour, which can be quite bland. I grate half a kilo of courgettes into a colander, sprinkle with a little salt and leave the liquid to seep out. Then I give them a good squeeze, before dipping them in flour, to which I've added breadcrumbs or polenta for a nice crisp. I pop them into two beaten eggs, along with some finely chopped parsley or dill. If you like, you can add some feta cheese, which is lovely. Into a well-oiled pan they go in small batches until they're crisp.

I also love to chargrill my courgettes, which I cut on the diagonal into long, thin slices, before placing on a hot griddle pan. I often pop a red or yellow pepper under a hot grill until it blisters (turn it regularly!), put the blackened pepper into a plastic bag, then gently rub off the charred outside to reveal the lovely soft, smoky pepper within.

7 Monday AUGUST BANK HOLIDAY

8 Tuesday

'I want to live my life so that my nights are not full of regrets.'
D.H. Lawrence

9 Wednesday

10 Thursday

I love a supper of strips of beef, stir-fried until they have
a lovely caramel colour, then served with griddled peaches
and feta on a bed of leaves. A complete summer meal
and so easy to do. Serve with a tangy vinaigrette – one
using balsamic vinegar goes very well with this. I sit on my
balcony to eat it and watch the world go by.

11 Friday

12 Saturday

13 Sunday

Taking the Plunge

The pastime of 'forest bathing' has become increasingly popular in the past few years. No, it does not mean walking around the woods in your swimming togs! It is the practice of walking mindfully in nature and it evolved in Japan, where they call it *shinrin-yoku*. You don't need any special equipment, apart from waterproofs and a pair of sturdy shoes: all you need is yourself and your senses, so that you can let nature surround you and switch off completely.

Dr Quing Li is one of the practice's best-known teachers, and the author of a book on forest bathing, *Shinrin-Yoku, the Art and Science of Forest Bathing*. He takes a daily walk in the forest near his Tokyo workplace, and for three full days a month, he takes off into the forests to reconnect with the natural world. But you don't have to go to those lengths. In Ireland, we are surrounded by nature and a simple walk outdoors will really refresh you. Even a hidden park or square in the city is perfect − sit under a tree, close your eyes and feel nature surround you.

14 Monday

'When you say "yes" to others, make sure you aren't saying "no" to yourself.' Paulo Coelho

15 Tuesday

16 Wednesday

I've been trying to improve my morning routine lately. It's not easy, because I'm a night owl, but I learned that getting up at the same time every day helps to set my internal clock. I've also learned that the snooze button is not my friend, as I crash back to sleep again. I've also learned not to reach for my mobile phone. Instead I stretch gently, take a few deep breaths and up I get.

17 Thursday

18 Friday

19 Saturday

20 Sunday

Your Holiday Garden

At this stage of summer, that gorgeous early bloom has turned a little tired and dusty. My plants look as if they could do with perking up a little. I keep them watered, but not overwatered. I poke my finger into the soil and if the top inch is dry, the plant needs watering.

If my lawn is looking a bit brown, I will water it early in the morning, but sparingly. Soaking a lawn isn't really necessary, and it wastes water.

Even though some of my plants look a bit bedraggled, I don't prune them yet, because they won't be strong enough for the first frost. I do deadhead my roses, however, as this encourages new growth.

If you are going on a short break, I love this little tip from the Royal Horticultural Society: simply wrap the plant container in a plastic bag, tying the ends around the pot. The condensation produced will be reabsorbed by the plant – genius!

21 Monday

'We might think we are nurturing our garden, but of course, it's our garden that is really nurturing us.' Jenny Uglow

22 Tuesday

23 Wednesday

24 Thursday

25 Friday

26 Saturday

Time to wash pillows, which I do twice a year. I hate lumpy pillows, so have had to try a few tricks to wash them without making them lumpy. First, washing them in twos seems to help – I'm not sure why! – and so does giving them an extra spin at the end of the cycle. If the pillow is washable, wash it on a warm setting – you don't need to blast the germs out! I then put them in my dryer on a low setting, with a few clean tennis balls, which really help to fluff the pillows up. Don't use Fido's chewed-up ones! If I'm not sure that the pillows are fully dry, I put them on my bathroom floor, which has underfloor heating, overnight.

27 Sunday

28 Monday

'Teachers open the door, but you must walk through it by yourself.'
Chinese proverb

29 Tuesday

I always get that 'back-to-school' feeling at this time of year, even though I left fifty years ago. Those patterns stay with us all, I think. I can still remember the All-Ireland finals when they used to take place in the third week of September. If Kerry were doing well, it was all systems go!

30 Wednesday

31 Thursday

September

1 Friday

2 Saturday

3 Sunday

Nuts, Whole Hazelnuts

A friend of mine has always walked in the Dublin mountains and there's a particular lake she loves that's surrounded by hazelnut trees. Come September, she'd always watch the little green fruit like a hawk to see when they'd be ready to pick, but when she'd return a couple of weeks later, they'd all have disappeared. She found her answer one day when she spotted a couple on a stepladder, stripping the trees of every single hazelnut and emptying them into industrial-sized containers! I think the lesson here is to share in nature's bounty.

I know that Nutella is a great favourite, but if you want to opt for a homemade hazelnut spread, you can make your own, using 200g roasted ground hazelnuts, 200g dark chocolate (70 per cent), honey or sweetener of choice to taste (some recipes recommend up to 100g of sugar, but I prefer a less sweet taste) and 375ml whole milk. If you want that creamy texture, substitute some of the milk with double cream. Toast the hazelnuts in the oven for ten minutes, then grind them to a powder in a spice grinder. Place a bowl with the chocolate and milk/cream mix on a saucepan of simmering water and allow to melt slowly. Mix with the hazelnuts and then add 50ml of honey or agave nectar or 50g of sugar or to taste.

4 Monday

5 Tuesday

6 Wednesday

7 Thursday

8 Friday

I love a quick mushroom pasta in September – it feels quite autumnal. I soak 20g of dried porcini mushrooms, which you'll find in your local deli – the flavour is fantastic. I chop a couple of shallots, pop them onto the pan with some olive oil, then add 200g of sliced chestnut mushrooms. When they are done, add the soaked chopped porcini, 1 tsp thyme and a glug of the porcini water, before stirring in a tub of crème fraîche. Alternatively, you can use 200ml vegetable stock and let it bubble and reduce if you don't like creamy sauces. The essence of mushroom and of autumn.

9 Saturday

10 Sunday

Autumn Fires

I have always loved Robert Louis Stevenson, having read *Treasure Island* and *Kidnapped* as a child. This poem comes from his book *A Child's Garden of Verses*, which he wrote in 1895.

In the other gardens
And all up in the vale,
From the autumn bonfires
See the smoke trail!

Pleasant summer over,
And all the summer flowers,
The red fire blazes,
The grey smoke towers.

Sing a song of seasons!
Something bright in all!
Flowers in the summer,
Fires in the fall!
Robert Louis Stevenson (1850–1894)

11 Monday

'If we treated ourselves as well as we treated our best friend, can you imagine?' *Meghan Markle*

12 Tuesday

13 Wednesday

14 Thursday

15 Friday

I like to let myself off the hook every now and then and prepare a bowl of popcorn, then settle on the sofa to watch a movie. I make a vow not to look at my phone until it's finished.

16 Saturday

17 Sunday

Love Lemons

I always like to have a few lemons in the fruit bowl. Their bright yellow colour is so cheerful and they have so many uses. When I consulted my favourite book, *The Old Farmer's Almanac*, I even discovered a few that I hadn't thought of! I've never sucked on a lemon to settle my stomach, for example ...

- If your pots and pans are looking dim, rub them with a cloth soaked in lemon juice to make them shine.
- Rub your chopping boards with the cut side of half a lemon to get rid of lingering smells.
- Lemon rinds placed strategically in your flower beds will deter cats – I must try it! I use a spray from the DIY shop that has lemon in it, but I'm sure rinds would be more eco-friendly.
- If your paintbrushes are stiff, soak them in boiling lemon juice for 15 minutes and they'll loosen up.
- Whiten your greying socks by boiling them in lemony water – they'll come up nice and bright.
- Lemons are also a great way to get rid of nasty smells in your kitchen bin – throw a couple of used lemons into it and it'll smell much nicer.

18 Monday

'It always seems impossible until it's done.'
Nelson Mandela

19 Tuesday

20 Wednesday

I love roasting pumpkins or butternut squash in autumn and eating them hot with a dab of butter, salt and pepper. Alternatively, I blitz the roasted flesh and then add to a 'soffritto', which is the base for Italian soups and stews, a mix of chopped celery, carrot and onion, sautéed gently for ten minutes. I pour on 1.5 litres of stock and bring it up to a bubble. A stick blender will bind it all together. Serve with some crispy sage leaves for an extra dash of flavour.

21 Thursday

22 Friday

23 Saturday

24 Sunday

'What greater gift
than the love of a cat.'
Charles Dickens

Getting Green with Houseplants

I've had to learn quite a lot about houseplants recently, now that I've moved to an apartment. The task has been made easier by technology, as there are a number of apps now that will do everything bar watering them for me, such as the Royal Horticultural Society's *Grow Your Own*. 'Never kill a plant again', one of them tells me. I'm in!

If you're a beginner, opt for a hardy trailing ivy, or an aloe vera plant, that won't drop dead if not watered for a while. Spider plants are another excellent choice, as are snake plants, with their tall, pointed yellow-and-green leaves, which 'thrive on neglect', according to one source. The yucca is another hardy plant that likes only a tiny bit of water. Don't do what a friend of mine did and stick your collection in the bath for a good soak – every leaf fell off and all she was left with was a collection of stumps!

Buy close to home – either cuttings or seeds from a friend or from your local nursery. This is more sustainable than buying the many exotic species that come from far away, wrapped in a ton of plastic.

I learned another great tip from the *Irish Times*'s gardening expert Fionnuala Fallon: if you buy a new plant, keep it on its own for a little while until you're sure it has no pests or diseases to pass on to the rest of your flock.

25 Monday

'Challenges are solved by rising to a level higher than the challenge.'
Deepak Chopra

26 Tuesday

Time for me to get myself winter ready. I used to clear the gutters
when I lived in Sneem, but thankfully that's one task I no longer
have to do. I still ring a gas fitter to check the boiler, I take down my
winter duvet to air and I get my woollen jumpers out of the chest of
drawers, which I fill with cedar balls to keep the moths away.

27 Wednesday

28 Thursday

29 Friday

30 Saturday

1 Sunday

October

2 Monday

3 Tuesday

4 Wednesday

The Irish Seed Savers Association (irishseedsavers.ie) is doing great work in Co. Clare, preserving and cataloguing our Irish heritage varieties of apples, beans, peas and other plants that grow well in this country. Some of their cuttings are 500 years old! They also have a catalogue of heirloom varieties, should you wish to look further into our native species.

5 Thursday

6 Friday

7 Saturday

8 Sunday

Sleep Time

If you're anything like me, you may have found it difficult to get a full night's sleep during the past few years. That 'background hum' of worry and uncertainty affected us all, I think. I've had to reset my schedule to make sure that I get enough sleep to function now that I'm back in the 'real' world.

I used to ring my mother every evening at 10.30 for a chat, but now that she's gone, that's sadly no longer part of my nightly routine. I really miss it. These days I make a warm, milky drink and turn down the lights while I get ready for bed. I settle down with a relaxing book and enjoy some quiet time.

I bought a set of blackout blinds, and they really do help – mind you, when I wake up, I have no idea what time it is! But they do mean that I don't wake up at five on a summer morning any more.

I don't like soothing music, so I opt for gentle talk – no news, just RTÉ's *Doc on One* (make sure it's a pleasant subject) and *Desert Island Discs*, which is excellent and has a huge back catalogue.

9 Monday

'As you get older, three things happen. The first is your memory goes, and I can't remember the other two.'
Norman Wisdom

---

10 Tuesday

---

11 Wednesday

---

12 Thursday

---

13 Friday

The fear of this 'unlucky' day is called *triskaidekaphobia*.

---

14 Saturday

---

15 Sunday

Rum and Raisin Walnut Cake

My friend Darina Allen has always been a wonderful baker and she gave me this delicious recipe for a warming autumn cake.

Ingredients

175g raisins
6 tbsp rum
275g butter
175g caster sugar
4 eggs

50ml milk
1½ tsp vanilla essence
275g plain flour
1 level tbsp baking powder
50g walnuts (shelled if whole)

You will need a 23cm tin, lined with greaseproof paper.

Method

1. Preheat the oven to 180°C/160°C fan/gas mark 4.
2. Soak the raisins in the rum for half an hour.
3. Cream the butter, add the caster sugar and beat until light and fluffy.
4. Separate the eggs and add the egg yolks to the sugar/butter mixture one by one, beating well between each addition. Whisk the egg whites until stiff and fluffy.
5. Add the rum, milk and vanilla to the egg/butter mixture.
6. Mix the flour and baking powder, then gradually add to the wet mixture, folding gently as you go.
7. Fold in the beaten egg whites gently, in thirds, before adding the soaked raisins and the chopped walnuts.
8. Pour into the prepared tin and cook in the oven for 45–60 minutes, or until the top is golden and the centre is set – a skewer inserted into the middle should come out clean.
9. Allow the cake to cool in the tin before tipping out onto a wire rack. It'll keep for ages in an airtight container.

16 Monday

'Glacann fear críonna comhairle.' / 'A wise man (or woman!) accepts advice.' *Irish proverb*

17 Tuesday

18 Wednesday

This year I have learned the power of saying no, but nicely. I used to say yes to everything, then overload myself and give out to myself about it. Now I say that I'll think about it to give myself time, then I see if it will fit into my schedule before replying.

19 Thursday

20 Friday

21 Saturday

22 Sunday

Samhain

From the carved turnips holding little candles that were
given to Irish children in the nineteenth century to
today's sugary spectacle, no Irish tradition has made it
further afield than Hallowe'en. As with so many of our
current traditions, the festival began as Samhain, when
the ancient Celts marked the passing of the season from
autumn to winter. The idea was that at this time, the gap
between the spirit world and that of the living was at its
thinnest – so ghosts could pass through.

When Christianity came, the religious festival of
All Saints' Day on 1 November and All Souls' Day on
2 November gradually merged with the older traditions.
The National Museum of Ireland – Country Life in
Castlebar has a display of homemade masks, which were
made out of cotton from old flour bags, with horsehair
moustaches. Fruit and nuts were also collected and, of
course, báirín breac. When my mother made hers, she
used to put a ring in it, but I recall other things as well.
A coin meant that you'd be rich within the year, a stick
meant you'd be beaten, a rag that you'd be poor. A tiny
cross meant that you'd be joining the priesthood!

23 Monday

'My humanity is bound up in yours,
for we can only be human together.'
Archbishop Desmond Tutu

24 Tuesday

25 Wednesday

26 Thursday

27 Friday

28 Saturday

29 Sunday

The clocks go back tonight, which signals the return of the
darker evenings. If you have Seasonal Affective Disorder, or SAD,
you might find yourself feeling a bit gloomy at this time of year.
A friend of mine bought a sunrise alarm clock that lights up very
gradually every morning, imitating the sunrise and setting her
biological clock, so that she feels fresh as a daisy.

30 Monday OCTOBER BANK HOLIDAY

'Ná bris do loirgín ar stól nach bhfuil i do shlí' /
'Don't break your shin on a stool that isn't in
your way.' *Irish proverb.* In other words, don't
create obstacles where there are none.

31 Tuesday HALLOWE'EN

November

1 Wednesday ALL SAINTS' DAY

2 Thursday ALL SOULS' DAY

3 Friday

My mother would have made her famous
Christmas cake by the beginning of November.
In fact, she made more than one, so that she
could ice it and give it to friends and family.
Her secret was to douse it liberally with whiskey!

4 Saturday

5 Sunday

Pat's Mam's Oxford Lunch Fruitcake

This delicious recipe comes from my friend Pat, who in turn got it from her mother. I have never tasted a nicer cake! Maybe it's because, like my own mother, she feeds it generously with whiskey. Even better, it uses the 'all-in-one' method, so it couldn't be simpler.

Ingredients

225g butter, at room temperature
225g caster sugar
5 eggs
350g plain flour
1tsp mixed spice
675g sultanas

125g glacé cherries – washed, dried and cut in half
125 mixed peel
25g ground almonds
zest of 1 orange
2 tbsp whiskey

You will need a deep 9 inch/23cm round tin or an 8 inch/20cm square tin.

Method

1. Preheat the oven to 170ºC/150ºC fan/gas mark 3.
2. Brush the tin with melted butter and line the base and sides with a double layer of greaseproof paper.
3. Place all the ingredients in a large mixing bowl and beat with a wooden spoon until well mixed (3–4 minutes). You can use a stand mixer, but Pat prefers the old-fashioned method!
4. Pour the mixture into the prepared tin and smooth the top.
5. Bake in the preheated oven for about 3–3½ hours. When you think it's done, insert a skewer into the middle of the cake. If it's ready the skewer will come out clean or with just a few crumbs attached.
6. Allow the cake to cool in the tin. When it's cold, turn it out, remove the paper and store it in a cool, dry place. If you like, you can pierce the surface with a cocktail stick and pour a few more drops of whiskey into it.

6 Monday

'People don't notice whether it's winter or summer when they are happy.' *Anton Chekhov*

7 Tuesday

8 Wednesday

9 Thursday

10 Friday

On this day in 1875, Pádraig Pearse was born; in 1871, the explorer Henry Stanley tracked down Dr David Livingstone; in 1982, Leonid Brezhnev, leader of the USSR, died.

11 Saturday

12 Sunday

Fun Green Gifts to Buy This Year

I know it might seem that I'm getting a little ahead of myself, but because it's busy in the hotel next month, I don't have a lot of time then for Christmas shopping. The great news is that there are tons of websites offering Irish products. This year, I'm going to make a real effort to be green. Here are a few ideas:

- I like to buy my nieces and nephews plastic-free shower goodies. Soap and shampoo/conditioner bars are surprisingly easy to find and they smell delicious. I also buy washable bamboo makeup pads, packs of reusable straws, water bottles, which can look very stylish, and those pretty tin or bamboo lunchboxes, which are much nicer than the plastic ones I used to take to school!
- For food lovers, I buy plastic-free wraps to cover bowls instead of cling film. They are made of beeswax (and vegan alternatives), and they look much nicer − and you can wash and reuse them. I buy reusable paper towels made of bamboo, because they last so much longer. I'm also a fan of reusable tin liners instead of greaseproof paper. In the garden, native Irish seeds make a wonderful gift: you can grow your own 'Balbriggan Brussel sprouts', for example!
- It's hard to find ethically produced chocolate, but there are a number of artisan Irish brands that are now being sold in shops and supermarkets. Look for organic, Fairtrade and palm oil-free, with recyclable packaging.

13 Monday

'In times of crisis, the natural world is a source of both joy and solace. The natural world produces the comfort that can come from nothing else.' *Sir David Attenborough*

---

14 Tuesday

---

15 Wednesday

---

16 Thursday

---

17 Friday

And ... breathe. I've become a big fan of simple breathing exercises to switch off anxious thoughts. I love the '54321' exercise. Take a few deep breaths. Look around you and name five things you can see, four things you can touch, three things you can hear, two things you can smell and one thing you can taste. Simple, but by the time I've done all that I'm nicely relaxed again.

---

18 Saturday

---

19 Sunday

20 Monday

'Laughter is the sun that drives winter from the human face.'
Victor Hugo

21 Tuesday

22 Wednesday

23 Thursday

'A snowdrop by the road today bowed gracefully
and high upon the wing up in the sparkling nothingness,
a lone bird began to sing
Can gentle spring be far away?'
From 'Winter' by Tommy Makem (1932–2007)

24 Friday

25 Saturday

26 Sunday

A Mindful Moment

As you might have noticed from the '54321' exercise the other week, I've become a fan of mindfulness over the last couple of years, because it is so quick and so easy to incorporate into daily life. After everything that's happened to us over the past couple of years, taking the time to just 'be' is so important.

I like to switch off from technology for a bit and put the phone away every now and then. I always thought that I didn't use it much, but then I got one of those apps – ironically – that times your phone usage. I was shocked to see that I used it for a total of four hours a day. Time to take a break! It takes a little getting used to, but I'd recommend it.

I have a friend who prioritises reading and makes the time to sit down with a book for one hour a day. He's very firm about this and has worked it into his daily schedule. Now, if you're a busy parent, for example, you might think that you'd never have that kind of time, but it doesn't matter what you do: it's making time for the things that are important to you that matters, whether it's a gym session or a coffee, a haircut or a hot bath.

27 Monday

'There is no sunrise so beautiful that it's worth waking me up to see it.'
Mindy Kaling
I'm with Mindy here – I am not a morning person!

28 Tuesday

29 Wednesday

30 Thursday

The garden often looks a bit sad at this time of year, but you can get outside and do a few jobs, even if the days are getting shorter. Take bulbs inside, cover delicate plants with fleece and if you have a vegetable patch, turn the soil over and nourish it in readiness for planting in spring. Don't forget to rake up the last of the fallen leaves!

December

1 Friday

2 Saturday

3 Sunday

Have Yourself a Merry Eco-Friendly Christmas

Christmas is a bit of a minefield when it comes to being sustainable. We do love our tinsel and our glitter! However, there are a few simple things we can do to help.

Buy a 'pre-loved' tree

A friend of mine once bought an artificial Christmas tree, and her children have never stopped giving out about it! However, even though you might think artificial trees are an eco-nightmare, you won't be throwing them out because they last for ever. Better still, if you look online at websites like Gumtree, you might well find a second-hand one.

Make your own decorations

I really treasure the little Christmas decorations my nieces and nephews made at school. Every time I look at a wonky Santa or reindeer, I think of them. It's easy to make your own, too. You can bake ginger biscuits, ice them and attach them to the tree with a length of ribbon – don't do what my friend did and put them down low, however – her dog ate them all!

Cook smarter

During the 'big snow' of 2010, I wasn't able to get out to buy my usual 20lb turkey and ham. The best I could do was walk to the village, so I had to buy whatever I could find there – and carry it all home! It made me realise how much food I was wasting. A smaller boned and rolled turkey was eaten by St Stephen's Day and the small bag of spuds and parsnips did six of us for dinner. We are encouraged to overdo things at Christmas, but really, there's no need.

4 Monday

'The way you spend Christmas is way more important than how much.' *Henry David Thoreau*

5 Tuesday

6 Wednesday

Time to clean my apartment before I put the decorations up! I get the hoover out, pop on the duster attachment and get to work. When the dusting's done, I'll take the decorations down from the attic, sort through them and remove anything broken or damaged.

7 Thursday

8 Friday

9 Saturday

10 Sunday

Deck the Halls

Putting up the decorations always reminds me of my earliest days as an entrepreneur. I was only 16, but I already liked having a bit of money in my pocket, so at Christmas, I used to make Yule logs, decorated with red candles, holly berries and spray snow from the famous Hector Gray shop in Dublin. One year, to my alarm, no berries appeared on the holly in the neighbourhood, so I worried that my logs would look a bit threadbare. I had no idea what to do, until I looked into my neighbour's garden and had a brainwave.

Miss Beggs was a retired insurance executive and keen gardener. She had a magnificent skimmia tree in her garden, which gardeners will recognise as a dark green shrub with hundreds of red berries on it. I'd use them, I thought, and no one will be any the wiser. Even better, the birds don't like its berries, so they wouldn't get eaten.

One moonlit night I jumped the ditch between our home and hers, a pair of scissors in my hand. I relieved the skimmia of its berries, then attached the berries to the holly leaves with fishing line and secured a premium price for my Yule logs. I should have given Miss Beggs a percentage!

11 Monday

'What I don't like about office Christmas parties is looking for a job the next day.'
Phyllis Diller

12 Tuesday

13 Wednesday

I love edible decorations on my Christmas tree: ginger biscuits, jellies, chocolate Santas or bells – the children love them – even if the tree is almost bare by Christmas Day!

14 Thursday

15 Friday

16 Saturday

17 Sunday

'It's not how much we give but how much love we put into giving.'
Mother Teresa

Christmas for Everyone

Over the past couple of years, so many of us spent Christmas separated from loved ones, 'zooming' instead of seeing our families in real life. Others spent the season alone, whether by choice or circumstance.

In the midst of all the drama, spare a thought for those who aren't mad about the season. Don't shove Christmas in their faces. Instead, ask gently if they'd like to join you for drinks or dinner, and don't worry if they'd prefer to be left out of it. For some people, the razzmatazz can be overwhelming.

Christmas is a time for tradition, but it's also a time to make new memories and to invent new traditions. If you don't like turkey, don't eat it – eat lamb instead, or fish, or whatever you fancy. You don't *have* to spend Christmas a certain way.

Try to do one small thing for those in need. You can volunteer to serve Christmas Day meals, or simply donate to a charity. You can visit a friend in hospital or walk a neighbour's dog – or simply notice when a friend is struggling and listen to their story.

18 Monday

'Santa Claus has the right idea. Visit people only once a year.'
Victor Borge

19 Tuesday

20 Wednesday

21 Thursday

22 Friday

23 Saturday

Our *At Your Service* Christmas special a few years ago featured Cork's famous Penny Dinners. It was so enlightening and heart-warming to see that small changes could make such a difference to people's lives. What an amazing charity it is, serving hot, nourishing food to those who need it most. www.corkpennydinners.ie

24 Sunday CHRISTMAS EVE

Before the Ice is in the Pools

A lovely, simple verse that captures the magic of winter
stillness and a mystical event that happened to Dickinson.

Before the ice is in the pools –
　　　Before the skaters go,
Or any check at nightfall
　　　Is tarnished by the snow –

Before the fields have finished,
　　　Before the Christmas tree,
Wonder upon wonder
　　　Will arrive to me!

What we touch the hems of
　　　On a summer's day –
What is only walking
　　　Just a bridge away –

That which sings so, speaks so,
　　　When there's no one here –
Will the frock I wept in
　　　Answer me to wear?
　　　Emily Dickinson (1830–1886)

25 Monday CHRISTMAS DAY

'Aren't we forgetting the true meaning of
Christmas? You know, the birth of Santa.'
Bart Simpson

26 Tuesday ST STEPHEN'S DAY

27 Wednesday

28 Thursday

Mum's birthday. It used to be something
of a family joke that she couldn't remember
whether it was the 28th or the 29th. How
lucky we were to have had so much time
with her.

29 Friday

30 Saturday

31 Sunday NEW YEAR'S EVE

ESSENTIAL CONTACTS

Name	
Address	
Mobile	
Email	

Name	
Address	
Mobile	
Email	

Name	
Address	
Mobile	
Email	

Name	
Address	
Mobile	
Email	

Name	
Address	
Mobile	
Email	

Name	
Address	
Mobile	
Email	

Name	
Address	
Mobile	
Email	

Name	
Address	
Mobile	
Email	

Name	
Address	
Mobile	
Email	

Name	
Address	
Mobile	
Email	

Name	
Address	
Mobile	
Email	

Name	
Address	
Mobile	
Email	

Name	
Address	
Mobile	
Email	

Name	
Address	
Mobile	
Email	

Name	
Address	
Mobile	
Email	

Name	
Address	
Mobile	
Email	

Name	
Address	
Mobile	
Email	

Name	
Address	
Mobile	
Email	

Name	
Address	
Mobile	
Email	

Name	
Address	
Mobile	
Email	

Name	
Address	
Mobile	
Email	

Name	
Address	
Mobile	
Email	

Name	
Address	
Mobile	
Email	

Name	
Address	
Mobile	
Email	

Name	
Address	
Mobile	
Email	

Name	
Address	
Mobile	
Email	

Name	
Address	
Mobile	
Email	

Name	
Address	
Mobile	
Email	

Name	
Address	
Mobile	
Email	

Name	
Address	
Mobile	
Email	

NOTES